GW00536219

THE LONDON DIPLOMATIC LIST

January 2022

CONTENTS

30108   024212339

THE LONDON DIPLOMATIC LIST

Alphabetical list of the representatives of Foreign States & Commonwealth Countries in London with names and embassy designations of the persons returned as composing of their diplomatic staff. Representatives of Foreign States & Commonwealth Countries and their diplomatic staff enjoy privileges and immunities under the Diplomatic Privileges Act (1964). Except where shown, private addresses are not available.

M Married or in a Civil Partnership
* Married or in a Civil Partnership but not accompanied by spouse or Civil Partner

AFGHANISTAN

Embassy of the Islamic Republic of Afghanistan
31 Princes Gate, London, SW7 1QQ
Phone: 020 7225 0095
Email: ea@afghanistanembassy.org.uk
Web: www.afghanistanembassy.org.uk
Hours: Monday-Friday 09:00 to 17:00

Consular Department
Phone: 020 7584 4443
Email: consulate@afghanistanembassy.org.uk
Hours: Monday-Friday 09:00 to 17:00

HIS EXCELLENCY DR ZALMAI RASSOUL
Ambassador Extraordinary & Plenipotentiary (since 11 January 2021)

Mr Abdul Khaliq Samandary **m** *Counsellor*
Mr Haroon Naderi **m** *Military Attaché*
Mr Sayed Mansoor Sayed **m** *1st Secretary*
Mr Sayed Rafi Eklil **m** *2nd Secretary*
Mr Faramaz Hussiny *3rd Secretary*

ALBANIA

Embassy of the Republic of Albania
33 St George's Drive, London, SW1V 4DG
Phone: 020 7828 8897
Fax: 020 7828 8869
Email: embassy.london@mfa.gov.al
Web: www.ambasadat.gov.al/united-kingdom

Consular Section
Phone: 020 7828 8897
Fax: 020 7828 8869
Email: consular.london@mfa.gov.al

Defence Attaché's Office
Phone: 020 7828 8897
Fax: 020 7828 8869
Email: aulonder@mod.gov.al

Police Liaison Officer's Office
Phone: 020 7828 8897
Fax: 020 7828 8869
Email: andrin.cenaj@asp.gov.al

HIS EXELLENCY MR QIRJAKO QIRKO *
Ambassador Extraordinary & Plenipotentiary (since 26 *August 2016*)
    Mrs Anxhela Qirko

Mrs Mamica Toska *Minister Plenipotentiary*
Mrs Alketa Lama * *Counsellor (Political Affairs)*
Mrs Mirela Ndini *1st Secretary (Consul)*
Mr Refik Golli *2nd Secretary Consul (Consular Services)*
Miss Fjorela Kastrati *2nd Secretary*
Mr Arjan Hilaj **m** *Defence Attaché*
Andrin Cenaj **m** *Liaison Officer (Police Liaison)*

ALGERIA

People's Democratic Republic of Algeria
1-3 Riding House Street, London, W1W 7DR
Phone: 20 7299 7077
Fax: 020 7299 7076
Email: info@algerianembassy.org.uk

Consular Section
The Portal, 5 Portal Way, London, W3 6RS
Phone: 020 8752 1177
Fax: 020 8752 8061
Email: info@algerian-consulate.org.uk

HIS EXELLENCY MR LOUNES MAGRAMANE **m**
Ambassador Extraordinary & Plenipotentiary (Since 21 December 2021)
    Mrs Ghania Magramane

Mr Ali Achoui **m** *Minister-Counsellor*
Lt Colonel Khaled Reghioua **m** *Defence Attaché*
Mr Abdelkrim Beha **m** *Consul General*
Mr Mostefa Boudib **m** *Minister Plenipotentiary*
Mr Mohamed Khelifi **m** *Counsellor*
Mr Toufik Derghal **m** *Counsellor*
Mr Mohamed Seghir Benghanem **m** *Counsellor*
Mr Mokhtar Latrache **m** *Counsellor(Chancery Attaché)*
Mr Abdenour Gasmi **m** *Counsellor (Chancery Attaché)*
Mr Hamed Oussama Salhi *1st Secretary*
Mr Ishak Dehibi **m** *1st Secretary*
Mr Djamel Alaouchiche **m** *1st Secretary*
Mrs Imen Dehibi **m** *1st Secretary*
Mrs Noura Smail **m** *1 st Secretary*
Mr Mohammed Rehamnia **m** *1 st Secretary*
Mrs Sihem Zibra **m** *Attaché*
Mr Touffik Slimani **m** *Attaché*
Mr Chakib Mahmoudi **m** *Attaché*
Mrs Zohra Abed **m** *Attaché*
Mr Khalid Ouled Elkheir **m** *Attaché*
Mr Abderrahim Mourad **m** *Attaché*
Mr Tarik Lares **m** *Attaché*

ANDORRA

The Principality of Andorra
Ministry of Foreign Affairs & Institutional Relations,
C/ Prat de la Creu 62-64, AD500 Andorra la Vella, Andorra
Phone: +376 875 704
Fax: +376 869 559
Email: Cristina_Mota@govern.ad

HIS EXCELLENCY MR CARLES JORDANA MODERO
Ambassador Extraordinary & Plenipotentiary (since 4 November 2020)

Ms Cristina Mota Gouveia *Minister-Counsellor*

ANGOLA

Embassy of the Republic of Angola
22 Dorset Street, London, W1U 6QY
Phone: 020 7299 9850
Fax: 020 7486 9397
Email: embassy@angola.org.uk
Hours: Monday-Friday 09.00 to 12.00 & 13.30 to 16.00
Hours Visa Section: Monday-Friday 09.30 to 13.00

Consulate General
46 Bedford Square, London, WC1B 3DP
Phone: 020 7291 8700
Email: info@consuladogeralangola-uk.org
Hours: Monday-Friday 09.00 to 12.00 & 13.00 to 16.00
Hours Visa Section – 21 Bedford Square Avenue, London WC1B 3AS
Monday-Friday 09.00 - 17.00

HIS EXCELLENCY MR GERALDO SACHIPENGO NUNDA m *Ambassador Extraordinary & Plenipotentiary (since*

27 February 2020)

Mrs Catarina Esmeralda Chinggufo Nunda

Mr Diogo José Paulo Cristiano m *Minister-Counsellor*
Mrs Maria Odete da Gama Tavares França m *Counsellor*
Colonel Rui Nelson Gonçalves m *Defence Attaché*
Major António Pascoal Chibia m *Assistant Defence Attaché*
Mrs Rosa Benigno F. Sobrinho * *Alternative Representative IMO*
Ms Maria Teresa Fonseca de Victória Pereira *Consul General*
Mr Sebastião dos Santos Kiala m *Vice Consul*
Mrs Lutilele Sara Vasco Cangombe Monteiro m *Vice Consul*
Mr Alberto Domingos França m *Vice Consul*
Mr Wine Garcia Soares da Costa m *Consular Agent*
Ms Elianne Tessa G. S. de Carvalho *Consular Agent*

ANTIGUA AND BARBUDA

High Commission for Antigua and Barbuda
2nd Floor 45 Crawford Place, London, W1H 4LP
Phone: 020 7258 0070
Fax: 020 7258 7486
Email: highcommission@antigua-barbuda.com
Web: www.antigua-barbuda.com

HER EXCELLENCY MS KAREN-MAE HILL
High Commissioner (since 10 January 2016)

Miss Ideka Arienne Dowe *Economic & Trade Attaché*
Mr Antonio Olsen Joseph *Political, Diaspora & Consular Affairs Attaché*

ARGENTINA

Embassy of the Argentine Republic
65 Brook Street, London, W1K 4AH
Phone: 020 7318 1300
Fax: 020 7318 1301

info@argentine-embassy-uk.org
trade@argentine-embassy-uk.org
culture@argentine-embassy-uk.org
politica@argentine-embassy-uk.org
pressoffice@argentine-embassy-uk.org
protocol@argentine-embassy-uk.org
Web: www.argentine-embassy-uk.org

Consulate General
27 Three Kings Yard W1K 4DF
020 7318 1340
Fax 020 7318 1349
www.clond.mrecic.gov.ar
clond@mrecic.gov.ar

Defence Attaché's Office (Military, Naval & Air Attachés)
65 Brook Street W1K 4AH
020 7730 4356
Fax 020 77824 8703
defence@argentine-embassy-uk.org

Representation to IMO
27 Three Kings Yard W1K 4DF
020 7318 1340
Fax 020 7318 1349
imo@argentine-embassy-uk.org
raomi@mrecic.gov.ar

HIS EXCELLENCY MR Javier Esteban Figueroa m *Ambassador Extraordinary & Plenipotentiary* (since 31 August 2020)
        Mrs Alesandra Marcela De Figueroa
Ms Carolina Perez Colman *Consul General*
Mrs Mariana Plaza m *Minister & Deputy (Political, Press &Protocol)*
Group Captain Martin Gomez m *(Defence Attaché)*
Mrs Estela Fernanda Millicay Resquin m *Minister (Political & IMO)*
Mrs Alesandra Marcela De Figueroa m *Minister (Cultural)*
Mr Gonzalo Ortiz de Zarate m *Minister & Deputy Consul General*
Mr Federico Franceschini *2nd Secretary*
Mr Martin Miguel Alemandi *2nd Secretary*
Mr Nicolas Abad m *2nd Secretary (Trade & Investments)*
Captain Rodrigo Arriegues m *Technical Adviser of Permanent Representation to IMO*
Warren Officer II Diego Alvaro Soler Mendez m *(Assistant Defence Attaché)*

ARMENIA

Embassy of the Republic of Armenia
25A Cheniston Gardens W8 6TG
020 7938 5435
Fax :
armembassyuk@mfa.am
armconsularuk@mfa.am
www.uk.mfa.am

His Excellency Mr Varuzhan Nersesyan, Ambassador Extraordinary & Plenipotentiary,
        Mrs Narine Nersesyan, spouse
Mr Gagik Kirakosyan m Councellor, Consular Affairs
Mr Hrachya Stepanyan m Counsellor
Mr Aram Araratyan m Third Secretary (Political and Economic Affairs)

AUSTRALIA

Australian High Commission
Australia House Strand WC2B 4LA
020 7379 4334
Fax 020 7240 5333
www.uk.embassy.gov.au

HIS EXCELLENCY THE HONOURABLE MR GEORGE BRANDIS QC *High Commissioner (since 3 May 2018)*
Ms Julie Heckscher m *Deputy High Commissioner*
Ms Sarah Sullivan m *Minister-Counsellor (Management)*
Mr Christopher Moore m *Minister-Counsellor*
Mr Christian Hirst m *Minister-Counsellor*
Brigadier Grant Mason m *Head Australian Defence Staff*
Commander Jennifer Hurst *Minister-Counsellor (Police Liaison)*
Ms Jennifer Mackinlay m *Minister-Counsellor (Commercial)*
Ms Nicole White *Minister-Counsellor (Liaison)*
Dr Olivia Samardzic m *Minister-Counsellor (Defence Science &Technology)*
Mr Jaycob McMahon m *Minister-Counsellor (Immigration)*
Mr John Swieringa m *Minister-Counsellor (Economic)*
Mr Kyle Naish m *Counsellor*
Ms Christine Shannon * *Counsellor*
Mr Daniel Holliday m *Counsellor*
Ms Jo-Anne Hardie *Counsellor*
Ms Tamie Balaga * *Counsellor*
Mr Craig Ferguson m *Counsellor*
Ms Johanna Rayner *Counsellor*
Ms Louise Male * *Counsellor*
Colonel Michael Bassingthwaighte m *Army Adviser*
Captain Paul Mandziy m *Navy Adviser*
Group Captain Adrian Maso m *Air Force Adviser*
Mr John Napier m *Counsellor (Immigration & Border Protection)*
Mrs Annalisse Sly m *Counsellor (Transport)*
Ms Marisa Dominello m *Counsellor (Australian Border Force)*
Mr Stephen Jay m *Counsellor (Police Liaison)*
Ms Anastasiya Nishnianidze m *Counsellor (Trade & Investment)*
Mr Andrew Tuohy m *Counsellor (Financial Intelligence)*
Ms Brooke Sharpley m *Counsellor (Defence)*
Mr Kieran Macdonnell m *Counsellor (Agriculture)*
Mr Robert McGrath m *Counsellor (Defence Materiel)*
Mrs Amelia Williams m *Counsellor*
Ms Desmene Fielding m *1st Secretary*
Mr Andrew Yong m *1st Secretary*
Mr Michael Abbot m *1st Secretary & Consul*
Ms Katherine Forsyth m *1st Secretary & Consul*
Mr Nicholas Williams m *1st Secretary*
Mr Alexander Macinnis m *1st Secretary*
Ms Kathleen McBryde *1st Secretary*
Wing Commander Dimitrios Xinos m *Assistant Defence Adviser*
Wing Commander Teresa Wynter m *Assistant Air Force Adviser*
Lt Colonel Colin Morrison m *Assistant Army Advisor*
Commander John Relyea m *Assistant Navy Adviser*
Ms Kristie-Lee Cressy m *1st Secretary (Police Liaison)*
Ms Katrina Pullen m *1st Secretary (Home Affairs)*
Ms Joanne Fielding m *1st Secretary (Immigration)*
Mr Jamie Ferdinand m *1st Secretary (Liaison)*
Mr Aaron Jenkins m *1st Secretary (Criminal Intelligence)*
Mr Jade Newman-Andrews m *1st Secretary (Police Liaison)*
Mr Brian Turkington m *1st Secretary (Police Liaison)*
Ms Louise McGregor m *1st Secretary (Police Liaison)*
Ms Sarah Rose *1st Secretary (Immigration & Border Protection)*
Ms Tanja Ferguson m *1st Secretary (Immigration)*
Mr William Woodward m *1st Secretary (Liaison)*
Mr Hamish Fejo *2nd Secretary*
Mr Alexander Jackman m *2nd Secretary*
Mr Andrew Cuzner-Davis m *2nd Secretary*
Ms Laura Howieson m *2nd Secretary*

Ms Jennifer Lee m *Executive Assistant (Consular)*

AUSTRIA

Embassy of Austria
18 Belgrave Mews West, SW1X 8HU
020 7344 3250
london-ob@bmeia.gv.at
www.bmeia.gv.at/london
Monday-Friday 09.00-17.00

Cultural Section
28 Rutland Gate, SW7 1PQ
020 7225 7300
office@acflondon.org
www.acflondon.org

Defence Section
18 Belgrave Mews West, SW1X 8HU
020 7245 9185
Fax 020 7245 9185
ma.gbr@bmlvs.gv.at

Commercial Section
45 Prince's Gate, SW7 2QA
020 7584 4411
Fax 020 7584 2565
london@advantageaustria.org
www.advantageaustria.org/gb

HIS EXCELLENCY DR MICHAEL ZIMMERMANN * *Ambassador Extraordinary & Plenipotentiary (since 1 August 2018)*
Ms Katharina Kastner m *Counsellor & Deputy Head of Mission*
Dr Christoph Weingartner m *Minister Plenipotentiary (Public Diplomacy)*
Colonel Wolfgang Weichselberger m *Defence Attaché*
Dr Waltraud Dennhardt-Herzog m *Minister (Cultural Affairs)*
Dr Christian Kesberg m *Commercial Counsellor & Trade Commissioner*
Mr Mario Gavenda m *1st Secretary (Political)*
Mr Frank Ortner m *1st Secretary (Administrative Affairs) & Consul*
Mr Benjamin Cristoph Harrer * *Attaché (Administrative Affairs)*
Ms Christa Marchardt * *Attachée (Cultural Affairs)*
Mrs Vera Maier m *Attaché (Commercial)*
Mr Guenther Sablattnig * *Attaché (Police Liasion)*
Ms Maria Kaefer * *Assistant Attachée*
Mr Thomas Heizinger m *Assistant Attaché (Defence)*
Lieutenant Colonel Christian Gatt Egger m *Assistant Attaché (Defence)*
Ms Jasmina Dzinic * *Assistant Attachée*
Ms Jasmin Lindmaier * *Assistant Attachée*
Mrs Susanne Stauder-Jentsch m *Assistant Attachée*
Mrs Sonia Szydelko m *Assistant Attachée*

REPUBLIC OF AZERBAIJAN

Embassy of the Republic of Azerbaijan
4 Kensington Court W8 5DL
020 7938 3412
Fax 020 7937 1783
london@mission.mfa.gov.az
Consular Section Tel/Fax 020 7938 5482

HIS EXCELLENCY Mr Elin Suleymanov m Ambassador Extraordinary & Plenipotentiary (since 18 August 2021)
          Mrs.Lala Abdurahimova spouse
Lieutenant Colonel Vugar Ahmadov m Defence Attaché
Mr Polad Mammadov m 1st Secretary
Mr Nijat Guliyev m 1st Secretary
Mrs Gunel Salimova m 1st Secretary (will leave her post on 28 December 2021)
Mr Rasim Mammadov m 2nd Secretary
Mr Zaur Safarov m 3rd Secretary
Mr Tural Ismayilov 3rd Secretary
Mr Gudrat Balakishiyev m Financial Attaché
Mr Samir Salakhov m Administrative Manager

BAHAMAS, THE

High Commission of the Commonwealth of The Bahamas
10 Chesterfield Street W1J 5JL
020 7408 4488
Fax 020 7499 9937
information@bahamashclondon.net
www.bahamashclondon.net
Monday-Friday 09.30-17.30
Visa: Monday-Friday 10.00-13.00
Collection: Monday-Friday 14.00-17.30

HIS EXCELLENCY MR ELLISON EDROY GREENSLADE QPM m *High Commissioner (since 17 November 2017)*
          Mrs Kimberley Michelle Greenslade
Mr Marchea Alexander Mackey *3rd Secretary & Vice Consul*
Mr Anthony Arthur Stuart *Tourism Attaché*
Mrs Kimberley Michelle Greenslade m *Tourism Attaché*
Miss Portia Lahernia Williams *Finance Attaché*

BAHRAIN

Embassy of the Kingdom of Bahrain
30 Belgrave Square SW1X 8QB
020 7201 9170
Fax 020 7201 9183
www.bahrainembassy.co.uk
information@bahrainembassy.co.uk
Monday-Friday 09.00 -16.00

Cultural Office
98 Gloucester Road SW7 4AU
020 7341 0770
Fax 020 7373 4210
info@bcao.co.uk

HIS EXCELLENCY SHAIKH FAWAZ BIN MOHAMMED AL KHALIFA m *Ambassador Extraordinary &*
Plenipotentiary (since 1 September 2015)
          Mrs Shaikha Buthaina Mohamed Alotaibi
Mr Hussain Mohamed Alam *Counsellor*
Mr Mohamed Ahmed Yusuf m *Counsellor*
Mr Fahad A Albinali m *Counsellor*
Mr Ebrahim Abdulla Ebrahim Alshaalan m *1st Secretary*
Mr Bandar Sultan Alhathal m *1st Secretary*
Mr Ali A Rasool Mohamed Alalaiwat m *1st Secretary*
Mr Haitham Tamimi m *2nd Secretary*
Mr Tariq Almuraikhi m *Attaché*
Brigadier Ahmed Hamad S Alrowiaie m *Defence Attaché*
Mr Manea Almanea m *Cultural Counsellor*
Mr Mohamed Saad Hasan Alnoaimi * *Attaché*
Ms Islam Ahmed Abduljabbar *Attaché (Communications and Media Relations)*
Ms Alyaa Hasan Yusuf Aljeeb *Attaché (Political Affairs)*

Ms Isa Ali Mohamed Jabour Almusalam *Attaché*

BANGLADESH

High Commission for the People's Republic of Bangladesh
28 Queen's Gate London SW7 5JA
020 7584 0081
Fax 020 7581 7477
info@bhclondon.org.uk
bhclondon@btconnect.com
www.bhclondon.org.uk
Monday-Friday 10.00-18.00
Consular Section Monday-Friday 10.00-18.00

HER EXCELLENCY MS SAIDA MUNA TASNEEM **m** *High Commissioner (since 26 November 2018)*
    Mr Tauhidul I Chaudhury
Mr A F M Zahid-Ul Islam **m** *Minister (Political)*
Mr Dewan Mahmudul Haque **m** *Counsellor*
Mr Swadipta Alam **m** *1st Secretary (Political) & HOC*
Mrs Mahfuza Sultana **m** *1st Secretary*
Mr. Mr A K M Monirul Hoque **m** *1st Secretary*
Ms Moumita Zeenat **m** *1st Secretary*
Mr Md Lutful Hasan **m** *Minister (Consular)*
Mr A F M Fazle Rabbi **m** *1st Secretary (Consular)*
Mr. H M Faisal Ahmed **m** Attaché *(Consular)*
Mr Md Ashequn Nabi Chowdhury **m** *Minister (Press)*
Mr S M Jakaria Huq **m** *Counsellor (Commercial)*
Mr Md Mahbubur Rashid **m** *Defence Adviser*
Mr Sohel Ahmed **m** *Assistant Defence Attaché*

BARBADOS

Barbados High Commission
1 Great Russell Street WC1B 3ND
020 7299 7150
Fax 020 7323 6872
london@foreign.gov.bb
Monday-Friday 09.30-17.30

HIS EXCELLENCY MR MILTON ARTHUR INNISS *High Commissioner (since 17 December 2018)*
Mr Charles Merville Morris **m** *Deputy High Commissioner,*
Ms Natalie Carolyn Cox *Minister-Counsellor*
Ms Cheryl Allyson Carter *Attaché*
Miss Sandra Yvette Forde *Attaché*
Mr Kyle Carlton Gittens *Attaché*
Mrs Natasha Diane Mayers *1st Secretary*
Mr Marc Anthony Kojo McCollin *Attaché*
Mr Lennon Andrew Chandler *Attaché*

BELARUS

Embassy of the Republic of Belarus
6 Kensington Court W8 5DL
020 7937 3288
Fax 020 7938 5985
uk.london@mfa.gov.by
www.uk.mfa.gov.by
Monday-Friday 09.00-13.00 & 14.00-18.00

Economic/Commercial Section
020 7938 5988

Consular Section
020 7938 3677
uk.consul@mfa.gov.by
Monday-Friday except Wednesdays 09.00-12.30

HIS EXCELLENCY MR MAKSIM YERMALOVICH **m** *Ambassador Extraordinary & Plenipotentiary (since 19 August 2020)*
       Mrs Irina Vasilkova
Mr Mikhail Metelsky *Counsellor*
Mr Andrei Miskevich **m** *Counsellor*
Mr Dmitry Shchepachev *1st Secretary*
Mr Maksim Gorely **m** *1st Secretary (Consular, Cultural and Humanitarian Affairs)*
Colonel Dmitry Luka **m** *Defence Attaché (Non-Resident)*

BELGIUM

Embassy of Belgium
17 Grosvenor Crescent, SW1X 7EE
020-7470 3700
Fax: 020-7470 37
london@diplobel.fed.be
http://countries.diplomatie.belgium.be/nl/verenigd_koninkrijk
http://countries.diplomatie.belgium.be/fr/royaume_uni
http://countries.diplomatie.belgium.be/en/united_kingdom

Office of the Flemish Community and Region:
Flanders House, 1A Cavendish Square, W1G 0LD
Flemish Community:
020-7299 3590
Fax: 020-7299 3591
Flanders Trade & Investment:
020-7307 7710
Fax: 020-7307 7711

HIS EXCELLENCY MR BRUNO VAN PER PLUIJM **m** Ambassador *Extraordinary and Plenipotentiary (since 18 May 2020)*
       Mrs Hildegarde Van de Voorde
Mrs Ellen De Geest *Minister-Counsellor (Political Affairs)*
Captain (Naval) Renaud Flamant *Defence Attaché*
Mr Peter Verbrugghe **m** *Counsellor (Political Affairs)*
Mr. Jeroen Deberdt **m** *Consul General (Head of Consular and Administrative Affairs)*
Mr. René Peeters **m** *Vice Consul*
Mr Matthias Vanheusden **m** *First Secretary (Political Affairs)*
Mr Benjamin Muylaert-Gelein **m** *First Secretary (Political Affairs)*
Mr Martin Duruisseau **m** *Consular Attaché*
Mr Bart Brosius **m** *Counsellor for the Flemish Community & the Flemish Region*
Mr Dirk Verlee *Economic & Commercial Counsellor for the Flemish Region*
Mr David Thonon **m** *Economic & Commercial Counsellor for the Walloon Region & Representative of WIB*
Mr Mohamad-Mounif Kilani **m** *Economic & Commercial Counsellor for the Brussels Region*
First Chief Commissioner Stanny De Vlieger *Belgian Federal Police Liaison Officer*

BELIZE

Belize High Commission
3rd Floor 45 Crawford Place W1H 4LP
020 7723 3603
info@belizehighcommission.co.uk
www.belizehighcommission.co.uk

HER EXCELLENCY MRS THERESE RATH **m** *High Commissioner (since 18 July 2021)*
       Mr Anthony Rath

BENIN

Embassy of the Republic of Benin
87 Avenue Victor Hugo 75116 Paris
00 331 45 009882
Fax 00 331 45018202
ambassade.benin@gofornet.com

London Honorary Consulate (see Honorary Consuls section below)

Vacant *Ambassador Extraordinary & Plenipotentiary*

BOLIVIA

Embassy of Bolivia
106 Eaton Square SW1W 9AD
020 7235 4248 Ext 100
Fax 020 7235 1286
embol@bolivianembassy.co.uk
www.bolivianembassy.co.uk

Consular Section
consulate@bolivianembassy.co.uk

Vacant *Ambassador Extraordinary & Plenipotentiary*
Mr Juan Carlos Crespo Montalvo **m** *Chargé d'Affaires*
Captain Carlos Aguirre Vega **m** *Naval Attaché*

BOSNIA & HERZEGOVINA

Embassy of Bosnia & Herzegovina
5-7 Lexham Gardens W8 5JJ
Tel: 020 7373 0867
Fax: 020 7373 0871
embassy@bhembassy.co.uk
www.bhembassy.co.uk
Monday-Friday 09.00-17.00
Consular Section: Monday-Friday 10.00-13.00
020 7373 0915

HIS EXCELLENCY MR VANJA FILIPOVIC *Ambassador Extraordinary & Plenipotentiary (since 1 September 2019)*
Ms Jasmina Sarajlic *Minister-Counsellor*
Ms Jadranka Jović Obrenović **m** *Counsellor (Consular)*
Col Nebojša Janković *Military Attaché*
Ms Biljana Lučić *1st Secretary*
Mrs Samra Koričić Mujkić * *1st Secretary (Cultural)*

BOTSWANA

Botswana High Commission
6 Stratford Place W1C 1AY
020 7499 0031/020 7647 1000
Fax 020 7495 8595
bohico@govbw.com
Monday-Friday 09.00-17.00

HIS EXCELLENCY REV. DR JOHN NDEBELE G SEAKGOSING **m** *High Commissioner (since 29 December 2018)*
    Mrs Lulu Talita Seakgosing
Col. Gilbert Molebeledi **m** *Defence Adviser*
Mr Godfrey Engliton **m** *Minister Counsellor*
Ms Gao Tlhongbotho Tsheko **m** *Counsellor II*

Mr Johannes Kabelo Moribame *Counsellor III*
Ms Ellen Tshotlego Seeletso *1st Secretary (Administration)*
Mr Moemedi Mokgosi **m** *Commercial Attaché*
Mrs Ntshadi Gloria Galebotswe * *Education Attaché*
Ms Gloria Senabye * *Administrative Attaché*

BRAZIL

Embassy of Brazil
14/16 Cockspur Street
SW1Y 5BL
020 7747 4500
info.london@itamaraty.gov.br
http://londres.itamaraty.gov.br/en-us/

Office of the Permanent Representative to International Organisations in London
14/16 Cockspur Street, 4th floor
SW1Y 5BL
020 7747 4544 / 4548
rebraslon@itamaraty.gov.br
http://rebraslon.itamaraty.gov.br/en-us/

Consular Section
3-4 Vere Street
W1G ODH
Tel 020 76 59 1569
cg.londres@itamaraty.gov.br
http://cglondres.itamaraty.gov.br/pt-br/

Office of the Naval Adviser
170 Upper Richmond Road
SW15 2SH
020 8246 4401
Fax 020 8780 0730
www.bnce.org.uk/

Office of the Air Adviser
16 Great James Street
WC1N 3DP
020 7440 4320
Fax 020 7831 8129
cabe@bace.org.uk
https://www.bace.org.uk/

HIS EXCELLENCY MR CLAUDIO FREDERICO DE MATOS ARRUDA **m** *Ambassador Extraordinary & Plenipotentiary (since 8 October 2018)*
              Mrs Lenice de Almeida Nóbrega Arruda
Mr Tarcisio de Lima Ferreira Fernandes Costa **m** *Consul General*
Mr Marco Farani **m** *Permanent Representative to International Organisations in London*
Mr Roberto Doring Pinho da Silva **m** *Minister-Counsellor (Deputy Head of Mission - Economic)*
Mr João Marcos Senise Paes Leme **m** *Minister-Counsellor (Deputy Head of Mission - Political)*
Mr Ricardo José Lustosa Leal *Minister-Counsellor (Multilateral)*
Captain Gustavo Sant Ana Coutinho **m** *Defence & Naval Attaché*
Colonel Nilton Diniz Rodrigues **m** *Army Attaché*
Group Captain Jose Henrique Kaipper **m** *Air Attaché*
Mr Augusto Luis Billi **m** *Agriculture Attaché*
Mr William Marcel Murad **m** *Police Attaché*
Mr Carlos Eduardo de Carvalho Pachá **m** *Counsellor (Trade & Investment)*
Mrs Christiane Silva Aquino Bonomo **m** *Counsellor (Deputy Consul General)*
Mr Otávio Augusto Drummond Cançado Trindade **m** *Counsellor (Political)*
Mr Rafael Souza Campos de Moraes Leme **m** *Counsellor (Public Diplomacy & Political)*
Mr Nicola Speranza *Counsellor (Environmental)*
Mrs Leticia Frazão Alexandre de Moraes Leme **m** *Counsellor (Economic)*

Ms Rodrigo Oliveira Govedise **m** *Counsellor (Education, Science & Technology)*
Mr Flavio Werneck Noce dos Santos **m** *Counsellor (Consul)*
Mr João Paulo Tavares Fernandes **m** *First Secretary (Cultural)*
Ms Veridiana Lhamas de Avelar Fernandes *1st Secretary (Consul)*
Mr Marcelo Adrião Borges *2nd Secretary* **m** *(Political)*
Mr Lucas Nunes Beltrami **m** *2nd Secretary (Multilateral*
Mr Renato Levanteze Sant'Ana **m** *2nd Secretary (Multilateral)*
Mr César Linsan Passy Yip **m** *2nd Secretary (Head of the Ambassador's office)*
Mr Hugo Freitas Peres **m** *2nd Secretary (Agriculture & Economic)*
Ms Fernanda Carvalho Dal Piaz *2nd Secretary (Corporate Services)*
Mr Flavio Biecker Barbosa De Oliveira **m** *2nd Slecretary (Political)*
Ms Maria Fernanda Vasconcelos de Almeida *Attaché*
Mr Francisco Carlos Leal * *Attaché*
Mr Roberto Ivens Mello de Souza * *Attaché*
Mr Luciano Gondim D'Oliveira *Vice Consul*
Mrs Helen Roberta de Souza da Conceição de Almeida **m** *Attaché*
Mrs Bruna Magalhães da Motta **m** *Vice Consul*
Ms Maíra Moscardini de Campos *Attaché*
Ms Lemirtes da Silva Candido *Attaché*
Mrs Renata Campos Nogueira Cid **m** *Vice Consul*
Ms Alice Amorim Campos *Vice Consul*
Mrs Janaina Gomes Fontes **m** *Vice Consul*
Mr Bruno de Toledo de Almeida **m** *Vice Consul*
Mrs Isabela Alves de Oliveira **m** *Vice Consul*
Mr Luiz Roberto Avelino Reciolino **m** *Vice Consul*
Ms Luciana Faviero de Lara Ribeiro *Attaché*
Ms Cássia Ayumi Furuta *Vice Consul*
Mr Marino Da Costa Aguiar Pizzani Prieto **m** *Vice Consul*
Mr Penélope De Melo Santos **m** *Attaché*
Mrs Marcela Malta Jucá Pimentel **m** *Vice Consul*
Captain Henrique Ferreira Costa **m** *Naval Adviser (Head of the Brazilian Naval Commission in Europe)*
Commander Rodrigo De Araujo Cid Santa Rita **m** *Naval Adviser*
Group Captain Jorge Mauricio Motta **m** *Air Adviser*
Captain Alex Azevedo Urbancg **m** *Alternate Permanent Representative to IMO*
Captain Hebert Araujo de Melo **m** *Alternate Permanent Representative to IMO*
Mr Andre Vale de Salles Andrade **m** *Deputy Police Attaché*

BRUNEI

Brunei Darussalam High Commission
19/20 Belgrave Square SW1X 8PG
020 7581 0521
Fax 020 7235 9717
info@bruneihighcomm.org.uk

Consular Section
20 Belgrave Square SW1X 8PG
020 7581 0521 (ext. 111)
consular@bruneihighcomm.org.uk

Student Unit
35-43 Norfolk Square W2 1RX
020 7402 0045, 020 7402 0953
Fax 020 7262 8406, 020 7706 0558
Monday-Friday 09.30-13.00 & 14.00-16.30

HIS EXCELLENCY FIRST ADMIRAL (R) PENGIRAN DATO NORAZMI PENGIRAN HAJI MUHAMMAD * *High Commissioner (since 20 June 2020)*
Mr Aizul Sofrin Abd Aziz * *Deputy High Commissioner*
Mr Pg Dato Yusof Sepiuddin **m** *Counsellor*
Mr Muchdieni Bin Haji Mohammad Salleh *1st Secretary*
Mrs Watriah Dato Paduka Zainidi **m** *2nd Secretary(Political)*
Mrs Norkhalilah Roslin **m** *3rd Secretary (Admin)*
Miss Dk Hjh Nor'aidah Pg Mohd Hassan *3rd Secretary (Finance)*
Mr Anuar Hj Mahmud **m** *3rd Secretary (Protocol)*

Mr Siti Khatijah Bara m *3rd Secretary (Consular)*
Mrs DK Maria Wati PG Emran m *3rd Secretary*
3rd Secretary (Protocol)
Mr Zainuddin Zainal m *3rd Secretary (Assistance Finance)*
Mr Khairul Amri Hj Bolhassan m *3rd Secretary (Finance)*
Mr Mohamad Hillman Husain *Attaché (Communication)*
Lt Col Mohd Hairy Erwandy Raya m *Defence Advisor*
Mr Maryadi Japar m *Defence Staff Assistant*
Mr Isham Ismail m *Attaché (Education)*
Mr Erna Sumarne Haji Sumardi *Attaché (Education)*
Mrs Rahimah Mohiddin *Attaché (Education)*
Mr Saidin Hidayat Abdullah Lasit m *Attaché (Education)*
Mrs Siti Nurbai Mornee m *Attaché (Education)*
Mr Mohammad Ariffin Matusin *Attaché (Education)*
Mr Muhammad Fahmi Abas **m** *Attaché (Education)*
Mr Mohidin Shamrin m *Attaché (Education)*
Mr Mohammad Dany Aimi m *Attaché (Education)*
Mr Khairul Sabrin Omar m *Attaché (Finance)*
Mr Md Anwar Mohammad *Attaché (Finance)*
Mrs Siti Norhafiza Othman m *Attaché (Finance)*
Miss Nurulhanisah Jali *Attaché (Finance)*
Miss Hazwani Hasnan m *Attaché (Finance)*
Mrs Dayangku Norhayati Pengiran Luba m *Attaché (Finance)*
Mr Pg Haledi Pg Aliuddin m *Attaché (Finance)*
Mrs Norsuriaashikin Ismail m *Attaché (Finance)*

BULGARIA

Embassy of the Republic of Bulgaria
186-188 Queen's Gate SW7 5HL
020 7581 3144, 020 7584 9400, 020 7584 9433
Ambassador's Office 020 7591 0781
Fax 020 7584 4948
info@bulgarianembassy.org.uk
ambass.office@bulgarianembassy.org.uk
www.bulgarianembassy-london.org

Consular Section
Fax 020 7581 9073
consular@bulgarianembassy.org.uk
Monday-Friday 09.30-13.30
Individual Inquiries on Submitted Applications 13.00-15.00

Commercial Section
020 7589 4875
Fax 020 7589 4875
trade@bulgarianembassy.org.uk
Monday 10.00-16.00

HIS EXCELLENCY MR MARIN RAYKOV m Ambassador *Extraordinary & Plenipotentiary (since 15 May 2019)*
    Mrs Mariana Nikolova
Mr Aleksander Manov m *Counsellor - Political*
Mr Petyo Varbanov m *Counsellor - Political*
Mrs Vanya Ilieva Smith m *1st Secretary (Consular Section)*
Colonel Kamen Ivanov m *Minister Plenipotentiary (Defence Attaché)*
Mr Nikolay Vanchev m *Minister Plenipotentiary (Head of Consular Section)*
Mrs Boyana Yaneva m *Counsellor (Social and Labour Affairs)*
Mrs Tanya Koycheva m *Minister Plenipotentiary (Commercial Section)*
Ms Maria Anguelieva *Minister Plenipotentiary (Commercial Section)*
Mr Hristo Dinkov m *1st Secretary (Home Affairs)*
Mr Milen Milov m *1st Secretary (Administrative Attaché)*
Ms Svetla Dionisieva *Counsellor (Director of the Bulgarian Cultural Institute)*
Mr Ivalyo Moysov *3rd Secretary (Political)*

BURKINA FASO

Embassy of Burkina Faso
16 Place Guy d'Arezzo Brussels B-1180
0032 2 3459912
Fax 0032 2 3450612
contact@ambassadeduburkina.be
www.ambassadeduburkina.be
Monday-Friday 09.00-13.00 & 14.30-17.00

HER EXCELLENCY MRS JACQUELINE ZABA NIKIEMA *Ambassador Extraordinary & Plenipotentiary (since 1 August 2018)*
Mr Assane Tamboura **m** *Deputy Ambassador*
Mr Ousmane Ba **m** *1st Counsellor (Consular)*
Mr Mambila Banse **m** *Counsellor (Economic Affairs)*

BURUNDI

Embassy of the Republic of Burundi
Uganda House Second Floor 58-59 Trafalgar Square WC2N 5DX
020 7930 4958
www.burundiembassy.org.uk

HER EXCELLENCY MRS ELISA NKERABIRORI *Ambassador Extraordinary & Plenipotentiary (since 11 OCTOBER 2021)*
Mr Jean Pierre Uwitonze *2nd Counsellor*

CAMBODIA

Royal Embassy of Cambodia
64 Brondesbury Park, Willesden Green NW6 7AT
020 8451 7997
Fax 020 8451 7594
cambodianembassy@btconnect.com

Consular Section
020 8451 7850
Fax 020 8451 7594

HIS EXCELLENCY MR KAN PHARIDH **m** *Ambassador Extraordinary & Plenipotentiary (since 7 September 2020)*
    Mrs Sokhany Ieng
Dr In Sophal * *(Counsellor)*
Mrs Sopheakleap Kong * *1st Secretary (Political)*
Mr Duong Chanthy **m** *Trade Attaché*
Mr Ti Honglim **m** *Second Secretary*
Ms Lay Channanika *Second Secretary*

CAMEROON

High Commission for the Republic of Cameroon
84 Holland Park W11 3SB
020 7727 0771
Fax 020 7792 9353
Monday-Friday 09.30 - 17.30
info@cameroonhighcommission.co.uk
www.cameroonhighcommission.co.uk

HIS EXCELLENCY MR ALBERT NJOTEH FOTABONG *m High Commissioner (since 2 October 2018)*
    Mrs Estherine Lisinge Fotabong
Mrs Anna Baninla Tasha Mbur **m** *Minister-Counsellor*
Mr Serge Cyrille de L'Assomption Bourne Wanmoh **m** *2nd Counsellor*

Mr Guy Elessa **m** *1st Secretary*
Mr Bonnard Carlos Tiangue Nganguen **m** *2nd Secretary*
Colonel Victor Enteng Mua **m** *Defence adviser*
Pr Humphrey Ngala Ndi **m** *2nd Counsellor (Cultural)*
Mr Guillaume Kimbi Loh **m** *2nd Counsellor (Communication)*
Mr Jeremie Nkoue * *2nd Counsellor (Finance)*
Mr Peter Ngwaya Ekema **m** *2nd Counsellor*
Mr Henri Steane Dina Imounga Mpollo **m** *1st Secretary (Communication)*
Lt-Col Marie Judith OWONO MENGUE * *Deputy Defence Adviser*
Major Alain Nagmou Pene **m** *Attaché*
Captain Casimir Augustin Menye Melingui * *Attaché*

CANADA

High Commission of Canada
Canada House Trafalgar Square SW1Y 5BJ
0207 004 6000
Fax 0207 004 6050
ldn@international.gc.ca
www.UnitedKingdom.gc.ca

HIS EXCELLENCY MR RALPH EDWARD GOODALE * *High Commissioner (since 25 April 2021)*
          Mrs Pamela Jean Kendel-Goodale
Ms Angela Gawel **m** *Minister (Migration)*
Mrs Sonya Thissen **m** *Minister-Counsellor (Political Affairs/Public Diplomacy)*
Ms Natalie Dubé *Minister-Counsellor (Commercial/Economic)*
Mr Derek Foote *Minister-Counsellor & Consul General (Management & Consular Affairs)*
Mr Stephen Wilhelm **m** *Minister-Counsellor*
Ms Claudie Senay *Counsellor*
Mr Gordon Shaffer **m** *Counsellor (Public Safety)*
Mr Robert Stevenson **m** *Counsellor (Migration)*
Ms Gillian Grant **m** *Counsellor*
Ms Julia Gurr Lacasse **m** *Counsellor*
Mr Ken England **m** *Counsellor*
Insp Wayne Stevenson **m** *Counsellor*
Mr Jonathan Sauvé **m** *Counsellor (Public Diplomacy)*
Mr Gorav Chaudhry **m** *Counsellor (Finance)*
Mr Aaron Rosland *Counsellor (Commercial-Ontario)*
Mr Klaus Buttner **m** *Counsellor (Commercial Alberta)*
Mr Daniel Perrier *Counsellor*
Mrs Janice Vogtle **m** *Counsellor (Economic)*
Mr René LaMontagne **m** *Attaché (Medical)*
Ms Rena Patel *1st Secretary (Migration)*
Mr Alexander Johnston *1st Secretary (Migration)*
Mr Sean Blane *1st Secretary (Management) & Consul*
Mr Gene Rudyk **m** *1st Secretary (Migration)*
Mrs Karene Uzan * *1st Secretary (Migration)*
Mr Steven Owen **m** *1st Secretary (Migration)*
Ms Jennifer Jordan-Saifi **m** *1st Secretary*
Ms Julia McNeill * *1st Secretary (Management)*
Mr Michael Williams *1st Secretary*
Ms Christine Dwyer *1st Secretary (Migration)*
Ms Sarah Hall *1st Secretary (Migration)*
Mrs Suzanne Elliott * *1st Secretary*
Ms Brittany Blackstone **m** *1st Secretary & Vice Consul*
Mrs Jennifer Wood **m** *1st Secretary*
Ms Xochipili Bryan **m** *1st Secretary (Migration)*
Mr Sean McLuckie **m** *1st Secretary (Migration)*
Ms Valerie Feldman *1st Secretary (Immigration)*
Mr Albert Wayne Price **m** *1st Secretary*
Mrs Laurie Blais **m** *1st Secretary (Migration)*
Ms Camille Ruest **m** *1st Secretary*
Cpl Mark Rysanek **m** *1st Secretary*
Ms Laura Lumsden *1st Secretary (Commercial)*

Ms Sonia Hooykaas *1st Secretary (Readiness & Security)*
Mr Serge Seguin **m** *Attaché*
Ms Catherine Hansen **m** *Attaché*
Ms Jovonne Lee *2nd Secretary (Migration)*
Ms Leilla Cranfield *2nd Secretary*
Mr Yassine Chemlal **m** *Attaché*
Mr Michael Kachmar **m** *Attaché*
PO2 François Gravel **m** *Attaché*
Brigadier General Paul Doyle **m** *Commander & Defence Adviser*
Colonel James Hawthorne **m** *Attaché*
Captain (N) Yves Germain **m** *Naval Adviser*
Lieutenant-Colonel James Price **m** *Assistant Army Adviser*
Lieutenant-Colonel Pierre Theriault **m** *Assistant Air Force Adviser*
Commander Dale Turetski **m** *Assistant Naval Adviser*
Lieutenant-Colonel Alfred de Boda **m** *Attaché*
Major Gregory Pappoulas **m** *Attaché*
Captain Della Boucher *Attaché*
PO1 Daniel Hyland **m** *Attaché*
Ms Sophia Arvanitis *Agent General*

CABO VERDE

Embassy of the Republic of Cabo Verde
Avenue Jeane 29 1050 Brussels
0032 2643 6270
Fax 0032 2646 3385
emb.caboverde@skynet.be

London Honorary Consulate (see Honorary Consuls section below)

Vacant *Ambassador Extraordinary & Plenipotentiary*

Mr Octavio Bento Gomes **m** *Counsellor, Chargé d'Affaires a.i*
Ms Dulce Helena Barbosa Vicente Silver Fernandes *Counsellor*
Ms Sonia Maria Lizardo Andrade *1st Secretary*

CENTRAL AFRICAN REPUBLIC

Embassy of the Central African Republic
30 Rue des Perchamps 75016 Paris

Vacant *Ambassador Extraordinary & Plenipotentiary*

CHAD

Embassy of the Republic of Chad
Boulevard Lambermont 52 1030 Brussels
0032 2215 1975
Fax 0032 2216 3526

Vacant *Ambassador*
Mr Detomal Nahogoum *Counsellor (Economic)*
Mr Bakhit Mahamat Saleh Brahim *1st Secretary*
Mr Hissein Abdoulaye Hartaka *Attaché*
Mr Mahamat Djourab Mallaye *Attaché (Press)*

CHILE

Embassy of Chile
37-41 Old Queen Street SW1H 9JA
020 7222 2361
embachileuk@minrel.gob.cl

Consulate General
37-41 Old Queen Street SW1H 9JA
020 7222 2361
http://chile.gob.cl/londres/es/

Commercial Office
37-41 Old Queen Street SW1H 9JA
020 7233 2500
Fax 020 7233 2501
info@prochile.co.uk
www.prochile.co.uk

Defence & Naval Attaché's Office
37-41 Old Queen Street SW1H 9JA
020 7292 1500/02
Fax 020 7434 0793

Military Attaché's Office
37-41 Old Queen Street SW1H 9JA
020 7233 3851

Air Attaché's Office
37-41 Old Queen Street SW1H 9JA
020 7799 5442
Fax 020 7222 3607

Carabineros Attaché's Office
37-41 Old Queen Street SW1H 9JA
020 7222 2361

Civil Police Attaché's Office
37-41 Old Queen Street SW1H 9JA
020 7222 2361

Office of the Alternate Permanent Representative to the IMO
37-41 Old Queen Street SW1H 9JA
020 7222 2361

HIS EXCELLENCY MR DAVID GALLAGHER m *Ambassador Extraordinary & Plenipotentiary and Permanent Representative of Chile to the IMO (since 3 August 2018)*
        Mrs Sara Crespo Ureta
Mr Julio Méndez m *Minister-Counsellor & Deputy Head of Mission*
Captain José F Fuentes m *Defence Attaché*
Colonel Carlos Parra m *Military Attaché*
Group Captain Ismael Barrenechea m *Air Attaché*
Captain Fernando Reyes m *Naval Attaché*
Captain Javier Mardones m *Alternate Permanent Representative to IMO*
Colonel Jorge Miranda Bulboa m *Police Attaché*
Ms Polly Ureta *Civil Police Attaché*
Mrs Karina Concha m *1st Secretary*
Mr Francisco Tello *1st Secretary (Deputy Consul)*
Lieutenant Commander Sebastián Bravo m *Alternate Permanent Representative to IMO*
Mr Gustavo Nicolas Poblete Bravo m *Commercial Attaché*

CHINA

Embassy of the People's Republic of China
49-51 Portland Place W1B 1JL
020 7299 4049
Monday-Friday 09:00-12:30, 14:00-18:00

Political Section
49-51 Portland Place W1B 1JL
020 7299 4055

Policy Research Section
49-51 Portland Place W1B 1JL
020 7299 4074

Press and Public Affairs Section
49-51 Portland Place W1B 1JL
020 7299 4088

Administration Section
49-51 Portland Place W1B 1JL
020 7299 4021

Consular Section
31 Portland Place W1B 1QD
020 7631 1430

Defence Section
25 Lyndhurst Road NW3 5PA
020 7794 7595

Economic and Commercial Office
16 Lancaster Gate W2 3LH
020 7087 4930

Cultural Section
11 West Heath Road NW3 7UX
020 7431 8830

Education Section
50 Portland Place W1B 1NQ
020 7612 0260

Science & Technology Section
10 Greville Place NW6 5JN
020 7625 0079

HIS EXCELLENCY MR ZHENG ZEGUANG **m** Ambassador Extraordinary & Plenipotentiary (since 06 June 2021)
      Mrs Mme Hua Mei spouse
Mr Yang Xiaoguang * *Minister*
Mr Guo Yuliang * *Minister-Counsellor*
Mr Yang Xiaokun * *Minister-Counsellor*
Mr Wang Qi **m** Minister-Counsellor
Mrs Bao Ling **m** *Minister* (Economic & Commercial Office)
Mrs Zhang Jin * *Minister-Counsellor* (Education Section)
Mr Yu Peng **m** *Minister-Counsellor* (Cultural Section)
Mr Jiang Sunan **m** *Minister-Counsellor* (Science & Technology Section)
Major General Su Guanghui **m** *Defence Attaché* (Defence Section)
Mr Tong Xuejun **m** *Minister-Counsellor* (Consular Section)
Mrs Zeng Rong * *Minister-Counsellor* (Press & Public Affairs Section)
Mr Feng Jialiang * *Counsellor* (Policy Research Section)
Mr Wang Hongwei * *Counsellor* (Policy Research Section)
Mr Zhou Feng * *Counsellor* (Administration Office)
Mrs XiaYuzi * *Minister-Counsellor* (Administration Office)
Mr Zhang Limin * *Counsellor* (Political Section)
Mr Lu Haitian * *Counsellor* (Consular Section)
Mrs Zhu Lei **m** *Counsellor* (Consular Section)
Mr Yang Ruiguang **m** *Counsellor* (Political Section)

Mr Li Xinhai **m** *Counsellor* (Policy Research Section)
Mrs Dong Wen * *Counsellor* (Policy Research Section)
Mr Pang Qian **m** *Counsellor* (Political Section)
Mrs Sun Wei * *Counsellor* (Press & Public Affairs)
Mrs Fu Jie * *Counsellor* (Press & Public Affairs)
Mr Yang Mi * *Counsellor* (Economic & Commercial Office)
Mr Ma Xin **m** *Counsellor* (Policy Research Section)
Mr Tan Ge **m** *Counsellor* (Science & Technology Section)
Mr Kong Xiangwen * *Counsellor* (Political Section)
Mrs Wang Xiaojing **m** *First Secretary* (Political Section)
Mr Du Zhengqiao * *First Secretary* (Political Section)
Mr. Ma Jian * *First Secretary* (Political Section)
Mr. Wu Zhonghao **m** *Second Secretary* (Political Section)
Mr Dang Xinkai * *Second Secretary* (Political Section)
Mrs Wang Limian **m** *Third Secretary* (Political Section)
Mrs Wu Xiaorui * *Third Secretary* (Political Section)
Mr Zhao Tianshu * *Attaché* (Political Section)
Mr Ye Wei *Attaché* (Political Section)
Mr Li Rui *Attaché* (Political Section)
Mr Wang Yanbo * *First Secretary* (Policy Research Section)
Mr Li Tao * *First Secretary* (Policy Research Section)
Mr Wang Zhixian * *First Secretary* (Policy Research Section)
Mr Zhang Yu * *First Secretary* (Policy Research Section)
Mrs Zhuang Xinyan * *First Secretary* (Policy Research Section)
Mr Lin Xinjie * *First Secretary* (Policy Research Section)
Mr Xu Cheng **m** *First Secretary* (Policy Research Section)
Mrs Qiu Xia * *Second Secretary* (Policy Research Section)
Mr. Sun Li **m** *Third Secretary* (Policy Research Section)
Mr Lu Xin *Attaché* (Policy Research Section)
Ms Long Jingni *Attaché* (Policy Research Section)
Mr. Luo Shijie *Attaché* (Policy Research Section)
Mr Qiu Ke * *First Secretary* (Press & Public Affairs Section)
Ms Xiong Jun *First Secretary* (Press & Public Affairs Section)
Mr Ren Chao **m** *Second Secretary* (Press & Public Affairs Section)
Mr Yang Yi **m** *Attaché* (Press & Public Affairs Section)
Mr Yan Kai *Attaché* (Press & Public Affairs Section)
Mrs Chen Wen * *First Secretary* (Administration Office)
Mrs Tian Lin **m** *First Secretary* (Administration Office)
Mr Wang Dayin **m** *First Secretary* (Administration Office)
Mr He Zhengquan **m** *First Secretary* (Administration Office)
Mrs Liu Ying * *First Secretary* (Administration Office)
Mr Song Jun * *First Secretary* (Administration Office)
Mr Sun Chao * *First Secretary*(Administration Office)
Mr Zhao Guanghui **m** *Second Secretary* (Administration Office)
Mrs Lyu Chunju **m** *Third Secretary* (Administration Office)
Mr Zhang Changtu * *Third Secretary* (Administration Office)
Mr Chen Wei **m** *Third Secretary* (Administration Office)
Mrs Xu Rui * *Third Secretary* (Administration Office)
Mr Zhu Dingkun * *Third Secretary* (Administration Office)
Mr Zhao Zhiqiang * *Attaché* (Administration Office)
Mr Li Junsheng *Attaché* (Administration Office)
Mrs Chen Ting **m** *Attaché* (Administration Office)
Ms Liu Jinge *Attaché* (Administration Office)
Mr Zhang Hao **m** *Attaché* (Administration Office)
Mr Xiao Jiawei *Attaché* (Administration Office)
Ms Tan Huiying *Attaché* (Administration Office)
Mr Du Jitao * *First Secretary* (Consular Section)
Mr Wang Binbin * *First Secretary* (Consular Section)
Mr Han Jianwei **m** *First Secretary* (Consular Section)
Mrs Zhang Ying * *First Secretary* (Consular Section)
Mr. Wang Peng *Second Secretary* (Consular Section)
Mr Xiong Pengfei *Third Secretary* (Consular Section)
Mr.Tian Chengbin * *Attaché* (Consular Section)
Mr.Chen Xiaoping * *Attaché* (Consular Section)
Senior Colonel Mao Fenghua **m** *Army Attaché* (Defence Section)
Senior Captain (Navy) Zhang Yanbo **m** *Naval Attaché* (Defence Section)

Senior Group Captain Dai Jinhua * *Air Attaché* (Defence Section)
Senior Colonel Gao Feng * *Assistant Defence Attaché* (Defence Section)
Senior Colonel Jiang Bo * *Assistant Defence Attaché* (Defence Section)
Colonel Chen Gaofeng * *Assistant to Defence Attaché* (Defence Section)
Colonel Zu Zhaonan * *Assistant to Defence Attaché* (Defence Section)
Colonel Luo Huan * *Secretary to Defence Attaché* (Defence Section)
Mr Zhang Yimin * *First Secretary* (Economic & Commercial Office)
Mrs Liu Na * *First Secretary* (Economic & Commercial Office)
Mr Gao Zhiqiang * *First Secretary* (Economic & Commercial Office)
Ms Liu Jingjing *Second Secretary* (Economic & Commercial Office)
Mrs Cui Xiangxin * *Second Secretary* (Economic & Commercial Office)
Mr Wang Dejun * *Second Secretary* (Economic & Commercial Office)
Mr Wang Chun m *Second Secretary* (Economic & Commercial Office)
Mrs Guo Zhitao m *Second Secretary* (Economic & Commercial Office)
Mr Chen Mingzhi *Third Secretary* (Economic & Commercial Office)
Mrs Tian Chang m *First Secretary* (Cultural Section)
Mr Yu Guo m *First Secretary* (Cultural Section)
Ms Mo Xia *Third Secretary* (Cultural Section)
Mrs Dong Mei m *Third Secretary* (Cultural Section)
Mr Li Guoqiang m *First Secretary* (Education Section)
Mr Du Changman * *First Secretary* (Education Section)
Mr Shi Song * *First Secretary* (Education Section)
Mr Wang Zheng * *First Secretary* (Education Section)
Mr Jin Kun * *Second Secretary* (Education Section)
Mr Gao Shang * *Second Secretary* (Education Section)
Mrs Luo Anna * *Second Secretary* (Education Section)
Mrs Ruan Shao *Third Secretary* (Education Section)
Ms Chen Chen *Attaché (Education Section)*
Mrs Wang Jing * *First Secretary* (Science & Technology Section)
Mr Huang He m *First Secretary* (Science & Technology Section)
Mrs Xie Huiping m *First Secretary* (Science & Technology Section)
Mr Tan Junyao m *First Secretary* (Science & Technology Section)
Mr Kong Jiangtao * *First Secretary* (Science & Technology Section)
Mrs Liu Ya * *Second Secretary* (Science & Technology Section)
Mrs Zhu Jingyun * *Third Secretary* (Science & Technology Section)

COLOMBIA

Embassy of Colombia
3 Hans Crescent SW1X 0LN
020 7589 9177 / 020 7589 5037
elondres@cancilleria.gov.co
https://reinounido.embajada.gov.co/

Consulate General
Ground and 3rd Floor, 35 Portland Place, London W1B 1AE
020 7637 9893 / 020 7927 7121
Fax 020 7637 5604
clondres@cancilleria.gov.co
http://londres.consulado.gov.co

Commercial Office
ProColombia
6th Floor, 2 Conduit Street, London W1S 2XB
020 7491 3535
Fax 020 7491 4295
london@procolombia.co

Military, Naval & Police Attaché's Office
3rd Floor, 83 Victoria Street, London SW1H 0HW
020 3170 6012 / 075 9018 8269

Vacant *Ambassador*
Mr Pedro Isidro Lopez-Perez m *Chargé d'Affaires a.i. & Minister-Counsellor*

Mr Ricardo Jose Lozano-Picon m *Consul General*
Mr Jose Ricardo Puyana-Valdivieso m *Commercial Attaché*
Mr Jaime Alberto Mejia-Alvaran m *Counsellor*
Captain Hermann Aicardo Leon-Rincon *Permanent Representative of Colombia to the IMO*
Captain Alfonso Cordoba-Garcia m *Naval Attaché*
Colonel Jose Daniel Gualdron-Moreno m *Police Attaché*
Captain Elmer Andres Cardozo-Ardila *Deputy Police Attaché*
Miss Adriana Sandoval-Trujillo *Cultural Attaché – 1st Secretary*
Mr Daniel Ricardo Cardozo-Escobar m *Vice Consul – 1st Secretary*
Mr Jaime Andres Diaz-Silva *3rd Secretary*

CONGO

Embassy of the Republic of Congo
37 bis Rue Paul Valéry 75116 Paris, France
0033 1 4500 6057
Fax 0033 1 4067 1733

London Honorary Consulate (see Honorary Consuls section below)

Vacant *Ambassador Extraordinary & Plenipotentiary*

CONGO (DEMOCRATIC REPUBLIC)

Embassy of the Democratic Republic of the Congo

020 7580 3931
Fax 020 7580 8713
missionrdclondres@gmail.com
info@ambardc-londres.gouv.cd
www.ambardc-londres.gouv.cd

Documentation & Cultural Resource Bureau(DCRB)
281 Gray's Inn Road,
London WC1X 8QF
Tuesdays 9:30-17:30 except on public holidays.
Identification and Biometric Data Collection for Congolese Nationals:
Tuesday 10:00-17:00

HER EXCELLENCY MS MARIE NDJEKA OPOMBO *Ambassador Extraordinary & Plenipotentiary (since 20 February 2017)*
Mr Eric Mulume Oderhwa Migabo m *1st Counsellor*
Mr Napo Ghonda Mbe Lukuya Ntela * *Minister-Counsellor*
Mr Hyppolite Olamba Ossomba * *2nd Counsellor*
Mrs Fanny Kayaya Beya * *2nd Secretary*
Mr Phinees Kabango Muepu m *Political Attaché*
Mr Fabrice Boluwa Londole * *Alternate Permanent Representative of the DRC to the IMO*

COSTA RICA

Embassy of Costa Rica
23 Woodstock Street W1C 2AS
embcr-uk@rree.go.cr
Monday-Friday 10.00-17.00

Consular Section
23 Woodstock Street W1C 2AS
concr-uk@rree.go.cr

HIS EXCELLENCY MR RAFAEL ORTIZ FÁBREGA *m Ambassador Extraordinary & Plenipotentiary (since 31 October 2018)*
        Mrs Laura Valverde Borbón

Mr Francisco Jose Masís Holdridge * *Counsellor & Consul General*
Mr Allan Ricardo Araya Sanchez **m** *Minister Counsellor & Consul General*

CÔTE D'IVOIRE

Embassy of the Republic of Côte d'Ivoire
2 Upper Belgrave Street SW1X 8BJ
020 7235 6991
Fax 020 7259 5320
TELEX 23906 Ivory Coast
Monday-Friday 09.30-13.00 & 14.00-17.00

Consular Section
2 Upper Belgrave Street London SW1X 8BJ

Commercial & Economic Section (Commodities)
33 Cavendish Square W1G 0PW
020 7462 0086

HER EXCELLENCY MRS SARA AFFOUE AMANI *Ambassador Extraordinary & Plenipotentiary (since 14 August 2020)*
H E Mr Aly TOURE **m** Ambassador *(International Organisations Section Commodities)*
Mr Nestor KOKO 1st Counsellor
Mr Feh Moussa GONE **m** *Minister Counsellor*
Mr Diomandé Gondo Serge SIABA **m** *Counsellor (Economic)*
Mr Euloge Innocent ATSE **m** Counsellor *(International Organisations)*
Mr David Jacques MIMRAN **m** Counsellor *(Economic)*
Vacant *(Counsellor)*
Mrs Safiatou Karambiri Financial Counsellor
Mr Kouamé Clément EHOUMAN, **m** Counsellor *(Commercial)*
Mrs Mea Marie KOUABLAN Counsellor
Mrs ASSOUMOU Née N'Guessan Flore **m** (*Counsellor)*
Mr Adou Hervé Stanislas N'CHO **m** 1st Secretary *(Tourisme)*

CROATIA

Embassy of the Republic of Croatia
21 Conway Street W1T 6BN
020 7387 2022
Fax 020 7387 0310
vrhlon@mvep.hr
http://uk.mvep.hr
Monday-Friday 09.00-17.00

Consular Section
21 Conway Street W1T 6BN
Fax 020 7387 0936
conlon@mvep.hr

HIS EXCELLENCY MR IGOR POKAZ **m** *Ambassador Extraordinary & Plenipotentiary (since 1 September 2017)*

Mr Davor Ljubanović **m** *Minister Plenipotentiary & Deputy Head of Mission*
Mr Tomislav Vlahutin **m** *First Secretary (Economic and Cultural Affairs)*
Ms Nelija Vržina **m** *First Secretary (Political Affairs)*
Ms Iva Gudelj *First Secretary (Consular Affairs)*

CUBA

Embassy of the Republic of Cuba
167 High Holborn WC1V 6PA
020 7240 2488
Fax 020 7836 2602
secembajador@uk.embacuba.cu
www.cubadiplomatica.cu

Consular Section
167 High Holborn WC1V 6PA
020 7240 2488
Fax 020 7379 4557

HER EXCELLENCY MRS BARBARA ELENA MONTALVO ALVAREZ *Ambassador Extraordinary & Plenipotentiary*
(Since 7 February 2020)
Mr Julio Enrique Pujol Torres m *Counsellor (Political Affairs)*
Mr Joel Hernández González m *Counsellor (Tourism Affairs)*
Mr Aristides Julian Hechavarria Torrijo m *Counsellor (Press and Cultural Affairs)*
Mrs Marta Castillo González * *Counsellor (Economic Affairs)*
Ms Isaskun Conseption Leal m *Consul*
Mr Michel Rodriguez Alonso m *First Secretary*
Mr Junior Rodriguez Fonseca m *3rd Secretary*
Mr Julian Alexis Ávila Velázquez m *Attaché*
Miss Layde Rodriguez Saavedra *Attaché*

CYPRUS

High Commission of the Republic of Cyprus
13 St. James's Square SW1Y 4LB
020 7321 4100
Fax 020 7321 4164
CyprusinUK@mfa.gov.cy
www.cyprusinuk.com
Monday-Friday 09:00-16:30
Consular Section, Monday-Friday 09:30-13:00

High Commissioner's Private Secretary
020 7321 4101
Fax 020 7321 4162
CyprusHCLondon@mfa.gov.cy

Political Section
020 7321 4126
Fax 020 7321 4164
CyprusinUK@mfa.gov.cy

Consular Section
020 7321 4100
Fax 020 7321 4160
hclconsular@mfa.gov.cy
For Medical and Sponsored Patients issues
hclmedical@mfa.gov.cy

Maritime Section
020 7321 4154
Fax 020 7321 4171
dmslondon@dms.gov.cy

Commercial Section
020 7321 4141
Fax 020 7321 4169
info@cyprustrade.co.uk

Tourism Section
020 7321 4170
londonadmincto@btconnect.com

Cultural Section
020 7321 4148
Fax 020 7321 4164

Press Section
020 7321 4127
Fax 020 7321 4164
hclpress@mfa.gov.cy

Cyprus Educational Mission
020 8881 6982
Fax 020 8365 8257
kea@schools.ac.cy

HIS EXCELLENCY MR ANDREAS S KAKOURIS **m** High *Commissioner* (since 01 September 2019)
      Mrs Kareen Farrell-Kakouris
Mr Nicholaos T Manolis **m** *Deputy High Commissioner*
Ms Melivia Demetriou **m** *Political Counsellor*
Mr Theodoros Gkotsis *Consul General*
Lt Col Theocharis Onoufriou **m** *Defence Attaché*
Ms Niki Savva *Counsellor (Finance)*
Mr Marios Stephanides *Counsellor (Maritime Affairs)*
Ms Riana Acarou *Attaché (Maritime Affairs)*
Dr Marios Psaras *Cultural Counsellor*
Mrs Vasiliki Kouma **m** *Educational Counsellor*
Mrs Diamondo Kyriakou Theodotou * *Attaché (Administrative)*

CZECHIA

Embassy of the Czech Republic
26-30 Kensington Palace Gardens, London W8 4QY
020 7243 7900
london@embassy.mzv.cz
consulate.london@embassy.mzv.cz
Fax : 020 7243 7926
www.mzv.cz/london

HER EXCELLENCY MRS MARIE CHATARDOVA **m** *Ambassador Extraordinary & Plenipotentiary (since 11 October 2021)*
      Mr Benoit Chatard
Mr Michal Strouhal *Deputy Head of Mission*
Brigadier General Vratislav Beran **m** *Defence Attaché*
Mr Pavel Duchon **m** *1st Secretary-Counsul (Consular Affairs)*
Mr René Dlabal **m** *Minister-Counsellor (Consular Affairs)*
Mr Tomas Kristlik **m** *1st Secretary (Political Affairs)*
Mrs Isabella Hubbard **m** *1st Secretary (Consular Affairs)*
Mr Martin Hosek **m** *1st Secretary (Cultural & Education Affairs)*
Mrs Magdaléna Kopicová **m** *1st Secretary (Political Affairs)*
Ms Michaela Chrtova *3rd Secretary (Head Economic & Commercial Affairs)*
Mrs Hana Kalasnikovova * *3rd Secretary (Political Affairs)*
Mr Michal Zizlavsky **m** *3rd Secretary (Media & Communications Affairs)*
Mr Premysl Pela **m** *2nd Secretary (Director of the Czech Centre)*
Mr Marek Timar *Attaché (Head of Administration)*
Mr Jiri Filip * *Attaché*
Mr Tomas Dokulil **m** *Attaché*

DENMARK

Royal Danish Embassy
55 Sloane Street SW1X 9SR
020 7333 0200
Fax 020 7333 0270
lonamb@um.dk
www.storbritannien.um.dk
Monday-Thursday 09.00-16.30 & Friday 09.00-16.00

Consular Section
Monday-Friday: By appointment only
Passports 020 7333 0200
Visas 020 7333 0200
Fax 020 7333 0266
lonambcon@um.dk

Defence Attaché's Office
020 7333 0228/0229
Fax 020 7333 0231

Representation of the Faroes
Tel. 020 7333 0227/0207
london@ummr.fo
www.government.fo/london

HIS EXCELLENCY MR LARS THUESEN m *Ambassador Extraordinary & Plenipotentiary (since 01 September 2017)*
      Ms Jeanine Arreguin Ayerdi
Ms Anne Dorothea Cathrine Bruun Aubry m *Minister Counsellor, Deputy Head of Mission*
Ms Catherine Jane Lorenzen Franklin m *Counsellor (European Policy and Financial Affairs)*
Mrs Marie Brink Norager m *1st Secretary*
Mr Morten Viktor Ranieri-Svendsen m *Counsellor (Commercial Affairs)*
Mr Esben Egede Rasmussen m *Minister Counsellor (Agriculture, Food & Fisheries)*
Mr Joakim Steen Barron-Mikkelsen m *Counsellor (Health)*
Mr Jacob Byskov Kristensen m *Policy Advisor (Energy)*
Mr Dennis Blicher m *Consul*
Brigadier General Jan Kazimierz m *Defence Attaché*
Mr Peter Mikael Ostenfeld *Maritime Attaché*
Pastor Mr Flemming Kloster Poulsen m *Attaché (Social Affairs)*
Ms Cathryn Jane Sanderson m *Minister-Counsellor (Representative of the Government of the Faroes)*

DJIBOUTI

Embassy of the Republic of Djibouti
26 Rue Emile Ménier 75116 Paris
0033 1 4727 4922
Fax 0033 1 4553 5053
webmaster@amb-djibouti.org
www.ambdjibouti.org

HIS EXCELLENCY MR AYEID MOUSSEID YAHYA m *Ambassador Extraordinary & Plenipotentiary (since 22 January 2015)*
      Mrs Manuelle Calligny

DOMINICA, COMMONWEALTH OF

Office of the High Commissioner for the Commonwealth of Dominica
1 Collingham Gardens SW5 0HW
020 7370 5194
Fax 020 7373 8743
info@dominicahighcommission.co.uk
www.dominicahighcommission.co.uk
Monday-Friday 09.30-17.30

Vacant *High Commissioner*

Mrs Janet Charles **m** *Acting High Commissioner & 2nd Secretary*
Ms Nakinda Daniel *3rd Secretary*

DOMINICAN REPUBLIC

Embassy of the Dominican Republic
81 Cromwell Road, SW7 5BW
020 7262 6856
pa@dominicanembassy.org.uk
www.dominicanembassy.org.uk
Monday-Friday 10.00-16.00
Consular Section
consulate@dominicanembassy.org.uk

HIS EXCELLENCY MR ELNIO MANUEL DURAN *Ambassador Extraordinary & Plenipotentiary (since 12 March 2021)*

Mr Francisco Manuel Comprés Hernández *Minister-Counsellor, Deputy Head of Mission*
Ms Ligia Auristela Reid Bonetti *Minister Counsellor*
Mr Gustavo Adolfo Sosa Ricardo *Minister-Counsellor (Political Affairs)*
Mr Pompillio Nuñez Berroa **m** *Minister-Counsellor (Education Affairs)*
Miss Nicole Jacobo *Counsellor (Trade, Investment & Political Affairs)*
Mr Joan Alemany Nunez *Counsellor (Financial & Administrative Affairs)*
Mr Alfredo Suárez Mieses **m** *Counsellor*
Mr Wagner Alexi Mendez Herasme **m** *Counsellor*
Mr Franklin Manuel Garcia Sosa *Counsellor*

ECUADOR

Embassy of Ecuador
Flat 3b 3 Hans Crescent SW1X 0LS
020 7584 1367 / 020 7590 2501 / 020 7590 2507
eecugbr@cancilleria.gob.ec
website: http://www.reinounido.embajada.gob.ec

Consular Section
9 John Sessions Square E1 8NQ
020 7451 0040 / 0207 278 2923
Fax 020 3503 0991
ceculdn@cancilleria.gob.ec
website: http://www.londres.consulado.gob.ec

Defence Attaché's Office and Permanent Representative to the IMO
Flat 4, 5 Lawson Close, Wimbledon, London, SW19 5EL
020 8715 3594
agderu@armada.mil.ec

Commercial Section
Institute for Export and Investment
5th Floor, 141-142 Fenchurch Street, London EC3M 6BL
020 3078 8042 / 0203 078 8045
london@proecuador.gob.ec

HIS EXCELLENCY MR SEBASTIAN MATEO CORRAL BUSTAMANTE **m** *Ambassador Extraordinary & Plenipotentiary (since 26 October 2021)*
Ms Maria Jose Jaramillo Moscoso
Mr Vicente Gabriel Villafuerte Manzano **m** *Counsellor*
Captain Boris Gustavo Rodas Cornejo **m** *Defence Attaché*
Mr Juan Carlos Yépez *Commercial Counsellor*
Mrs Carolina Jacqueline Troya Palacios **m** *2nd Secretary (Trade Officer)*

Mr Bolivar Urquizo Tenesaca **m** *2nd Secretary (Consul)*
Ms Maritza Del Rocio Arauz Castro *Administrative Attaché*

EGYPT

Embassy of the Arab Republic of Egypt
26 South Street, W1K 1DW
Tel.: 020 7499 3304/2401
Fax: 020 7491 1542
E-mail address: egtamboff@gmail.com
           Egyemb2020@gmail.com
Opening Hours: Monday-Friday 9:00-17:00

Consulate General
Visas, Legalisations, Egyptian Nationals
2 Lowndes Street, SW1X 9ET
Tel: 020 7235 9719
Fax: 020 7235 5684
E-mail: info@egyptconsulate.co.uk

Defence Office:
24 South Street, W1K 1DN
Tel: 020 7493 2649
Fax: 020 7495 3573
E-mail: egyptiandefenseoffice.uk@gmail.com

Commercial Office:
23 South Street, W1K 2XD
Tel: 020 7499 3002
Fax: 020 7493 8110
E-mail: london@ecs.gov.eg

Medical Office:
47 Longridge Road, SW5 9SD
Tel: 020 7370 6944
Fax: 020 7370 36
E-mail: info@egmedoffice.org

Press & Information Office
3rd Floor
4 Chesterfield Gardens, W1J 5BG
Tel: 020 7409 2236
Fax: 020 7493 7456
E-mail: info@egpressoffice.com

Cultural Office:
4 Chesterfield Gardens, W1J 5BG
Tel: 020 7491 7720
Fax: 020 7408 1335
E-mail: administration@egyptcultue.org.uk

State Tourist Bureau:
170 Piccadilly, W1J 9EJ
Tel: 020 7493 5283
Fax: 020 7408 0295
E-mail: info@gotoegypt.org

HIS EXCELLENCY MR SHERIF AHMED MAHMOUD KAMEL **m** *Ambassador Extraordinary & Plenipotentiary*
(Since 16th December 2021)
        Mrs. Heba Ahmed Mohamed Ismail
Mr Ahmed Ezzat Elkotb Salem **m** *Counsellor (DHM)*
Mr Ibrahim Ahmed Ibrahim Khalil Eldiwany *Counsellor*

Mr Ibrahim M.A.I Salem m *Counsellor*
Mrs Heba Tayea Ahmed Ramadan m *Counsellor*
Mr Mohamed Ahmed Mohamed Gad m *Counsellor*
Mr Mohamed H. I. Eid m *1st Secretary*
Ms Asmaa S.M. Zayed *2nd Secretary*
Mr. Ahmed M.A.ElAboulnaga *3rd Secretary*
Mr Tarek F.A. Youssef m *Consul General*
Mrs Jouman Asser Abdelhady Nigmeldeen m *Consul*
Mr Mohamed Raafat Ragab Hussnien * *Consul*
Commodore Sameh Soliman Mohamed Soliman m *Defence Attaché*
Col Dr. Ahmed Fathy Ahmed Abdelkader m *Assistant Defence Attaché*
Col Mohamed Osama Elsayed Aly m *Assistant Defence Attaché*
Col Hany Mohamed Mohamed Hassanin m *Assistant Defence Attaché*
Lt Col Ahmed Abdou Ibrahim Elnagdy m *Assistant Defence Attaché*
Lt Col .Pilot Ahmed Mohamed Sayed Omar m *Assistant Defence Attaché*
Major Ahmed Adel Ahmed Elsayed m *Assistant Defence Attaché*
Major Mohamed Mahmoud Mohamed Ahmed m *Assistant Defence Attaché*
Dr Rasha Kamal Mohamed A. Elshiekh * *Cultural Attaché*
Mr Tamer Mostafa Mohamed Ali m *Minister Plenipotentiary (Commercial)*
Mr Ahmed Salah Elsayed Eid m *3rd Secretary (Commercial)*
Mr Gaber Yusef Haider Alkashaht m *Attaché (Press & Information)*
Mr Mohamed Mohsen Mohamed Ali Ismael m *Tourism Attaché*
Mr Hossam Ahmed R A Elshinnawy m *Administrative & Financial Attaché*
Mr Mahmoud Mohamed Ibrahim Afifi m *Administrative & Financial Attaché*
Mr Wael Abdelfattah Ibrahim Rashed m *Administrative & Financial Attaché*
Mr Mohamed A. M. A. M. Reyad m *Administrative & Financial Attaché*
Mr Mmdouh Elsayed Ibrahim * *Administrative & Financial Attaché*
Mr Hesham Zakaria A. Elmassry * *Administrative Attaché*
Mr Mohamed A. Abdallatif Mohamed m *Administrative & Financial Attaché*
Mr Mohamed A. Omran Sarhan m *Administrative & Financial Attaché*
Mrs Soheir M. A. Ragab m *Administrative & Financial Attaché (Consulate)*
Mrs Naglaa Atta Moustafa Elkady * *Administrative & Financial Attaché (Consulate*
Mr Yousri A. K. Hozayen m *Administrative & Financial Attaché (Consulate)*
Mr Said M. S. Elhamzawy m *Administrative & Financial Attaché (Consulate)*
Ms Marwa S. A. Ammar *Administrative & Financial Attaché (Consulate)*
Mr Hatem Hosny Aly Hassan m *Administrative & Financial Attaché*
Mrs Eman Abdelghany Abdelkader Loueloue * *Administrative & Financial Attaché*
Mr Mahmoud Gamal A. Ahmed m *Administrative Attaché (Commercial))*
Mrs Doaa Mahmoud Mahmoud Sharaky * *Administrative Attaché (Cultural)*

EL SALVADOR

Embassy of El Salvador
8 Dorset Square 1st & 2nd Floors NW1 6PU
020 7224 9800
embajadalondres@rree.gob.sv
elsalvador.embassy@gmail.com
Monday-Friday 09.30-17.30

HER EXCELLENCY MRS VANESSA EUGENIA INTERIANO ELFARNAWANY m *Ambassador Extraordinary & Plenipotentiary (since 7 December 2020)*
        Mr Mohamed Taha Elfarnawany
Miss Gabriela Maria Ramirez-Lazo *Minister-Counsellor*
Miss Astrid Veronica Almendares Rivas *Counsellor*
Miss Amy Raquel Chicas Polanco *Counsellor*
Miss Andrea Del Rocio Moreno Ancalmo *3rd Secretary*
Miss Andrea Carolina Duran Nuila *Consul*

EQUATORIAL GUINEA

Embassy of the Republic of Equatorial Guinea
13 Park Place St James' SW1A 1LP
020 7659 9090
visa@egembassy.london

www.embassyofequatorialguinea.co.uk
Monday-Friday 09.30-15.00

Vacant Ambassador *Extraordinary & Plenipotentiary*
Mrs Maria Jesús Diallo Besari * *First Secretary & Chargé d'Affaires a.i.*
Mr Pio Estéfano Mba Ndong Nvomo **m** *Second Secretary*
Mr Pedro Oscar Mba Edjang Ngoho * *Financial Attaché*

ERITREA

Embassy of the State of Eritrea
96 White Lion Street N1 9PF
020 7713 0096
Fax 020 7713 0161
www.eritrean-embassy.org.uk
pa.ambassador@eritreanembassyuk.org

HIS EXCELLENCY MR ESTIFANOS HABTEMARIAM GHEBREYESUS * *Ambassador Extraordinary & Plenipotentiary (since 23 September 2014)*
Mr Salih Abdalla Saad * *1st Secretary*

ESTONIA

Embassy of Estonia
44 Queen's Gate Terrace, London, SW7 5PJ
020 7589 3428
Fax 020 7589 3430
London.mfa.ee
e-mail: london@mfa.ee

HIS EXCELLENCY MR VILJAR LUBI *Ambassador Extraordinary & Plenipotentiary (since 1 August 2021)*
Ms Inga Bowden **m** *Deputy Head of Mission*
Ms Hellika Kirt **m** *Consul*
Ms Agaate Antson **m** *First Secretary (Economic Affairs)*
Ms Kersti Kirs **m** *Counsellor (Cultural)*
Lt Col. Meelis Vilippus * *Defence Attaché*

ESWATINI

Kingdom of Eswatini High Commission
20 Buckingham Gate SW1E 6LB
Tel: 020 7630 6611
Fax 020 7630 6564
Email: eswatinilondonhc@gmail,com
Monday-Thursday 09.00-16.30 & Friday 09.00-16.00

Vacant *High Commissioner*
Ms Temnotfo L. C. Nkambule *Counsellor*
Ms Sithembile Prudence Lushaba *1st Secretary (Information)*
Mr Mandla Stanley Dlamini **m** *3rd Secretary*
Mrs Ruth N. Kunene **m** *Administrative Attaché*
HRH Qethuka Dlamini *Education Attaché*

ETHIOPIA

Embassy of the Federal Democratic Republic of Ethiopia
17 Princes Gate, London, SW7 1PZ
Phone: 020 7589 7212
Fax: 020 7584 7054
Email: info@ethioembassy.org.uk
Web: www.ethioembassy.org.uk

Hours: Monday-Friday 09.00 to 17.00

Consular Department
Phone: 020 7838 3895
Hours: Monday-Friday 9.00 to 13.00 & 14.00 to 16.00

Trade and Investment Department
Phone: 020 7838 3870

Press Office
Phone: 020 7838 3883

HIS EXCELLENCY MR TEFERI MELESSE DESTA m
Ambassador Extraordinary & Plenipotentiary (since 12 September 2020)
        Mrs Mekdes Amaha Yitbarek

Mr Beyene G Meskele Mada * *Deputy Head of Mission*
Mrs Roza Yerukneh Alemu * *Minister*
Mr Araya Gebregziabher Kidane *Minister*
Mrs Fortuna Dibaco Cizare * *Minister*
Mrs Nardos Ayalew Belay m *Minister Counsellor*
Mr Meknnen Amare Gebretsion m *Minister Counsellor*
Mrs Workaferahu Aklilu Derseh m *Minister Counsellor (Business Diplomacy)*
Mr Tesfaye Besmah Wubie m *Minister Counsellor (Finance Section)*
Mr Mesfin Haile Tesfay *Counsellor (Consular)*
Ms Tsehaye Tadsse Andarga *1st Secretary (Consular)*
Mr Getachew Meseret Anley *2nd Secretary*
Mr Dimru Bekele Aschenaki m *3rd Secretary (Consular Affairs)*
Mrs Banchayu Negash Tibebu m *3rd Secretary (Ambassador's Office)*
Mrs Leul Gebregiorgis Gebregziabeher *Attaché*

EUROPEAN UNION
Delegation of the European Union to the United Kingdom
Europe House 32 Smith Square SW1P 3EU
020 7973 1992
Email: Delegation-United-Kingdom@eeas.europa.eu

HIS EXCELLENCY MR JOÃO VALE DE ALMEIDA m *Ambassador Extraordinary and Plenipotentiary (since 1 February 2021)*
        Mrs Maria Ana Jara De Carvalho
Ms Nicole Mannion *Deputy Head of Mission*
Mr Adebayo Babajide m *Minister, Head of Political Section*
Mr Lionel Mesnildrey m *Minister Counsellor, Head of EU Policies 2 Section*
Mrs Marie Colette Fitzgerald m *Minister Counsellor*
Mrs Beatrice Covassi m *Minister Counsellor*
Mr Per Eckefeldt m *Minister Counsellor*
Mr Federico Bianchi m *First Counsellor, Head of Press and Information Section*
Mr Jaime de Villota Ruiz m *First Counsellor, Head of EU Policies 1 Section*
Mr Andrea Amelio *First Counsellor*
Ms Marie-Laure de Bergh m *First Counsellor*
Mr Cyril Robin-Champigneul m *First Counsellor*
Ms Kristin Vandenbergen m *First Counsellor*
Mr Elias Centellas-Martinez m *Counsellor*
Ms Annelene Damen *Counsellor*
Mr Daniel Fleischer-Ambrus m *Counsellor*
Ms Justyna Lawniczak m *Counsellor*
Mr Bart Vodderie m *Counsellor*
Mr Charles Canonne m *First Secretary*
Ms Albena Dimitrova-Borisova m *First Secretary*
Mr Emilien Gasc *First Secretary*
Ms Noura Rouissi *First Secretary*
Ms Marit Sillavee m *First Secretary*
Mr Jan Tatum Krauss m *First Secretary*
Ms Isabella Torta m *First Secretary*

Ms Beatrice Neven *Attaché Head of Administration Section*
Ms Kristina Vlondis *Attaché*
Ms Veronica De Ranieri *Assistant Attaché*
Ms Dako Mozagba **m** *Assistant Attaché*
Mr Guy Charles Marhic **m** *European Central Bank Representative*

FIJI

High Commission of the Republic of Fiji
34 Hyde Park Gate SW7 5DN
020 7584 3661
Fax 020 7584 2838
mail@fijihighcommission.org.uk
www.fijihighcommission.org.uk
Monday-Friday 09.30-13.00 & 14.00-17.00

Consular Section
020 75843661 ext 5340/5347

HIS EXCELLENCY MR JITOKO CAKACAKABALAVU TIKOLEVU **m** *High Commissioner (Since 30 January 2016)*
      Mrs Luisa Molidrau Tikolevu
Mrs Paulini Tala Tokaduadua Cakacaka **m** *1st Secretary*
Ms Florieann Rose Cecelia Wilson *2nd Secretary*

FINLAND

Embassy of Finland

38 Chesham Place SW1X 8HW
020 7838 6200
sanomat.lon@formin.fi
www.finemb.org.uk
Monday-Friday 09.00-16.00

Finland Trade Centre

Kensington Pavilion
96 Kensington High Street W8 4SG
Mr Harri Lanning *Senior Director, Head of Region*
harri.lanning@businessfinland.fi

HIS EXCELLENCY MR JUKKA REINO SIUKOSAARI **m** *Ambassador Extraordinary & Plenipotentiary (since 1 September 2021).*
      Mrs Mariella Siukosaari
Mr Vesa Jaakko Vasara *Minister-Counsellor & Deputy Head of Mission*
Mr Jukka Matias Pajarinen **m** *Counsellor (Political Affairs)*
Mrs Terhi Elina Bunders **m** *Counsellor (Economic Affairs)*
Mrs Leea Eveliina Lamminpää **m** *1st Secretary (Political Affairs)*
Mrs Heli Ilona Suominen **m** *Press Counsellor*
Mrs Sari Kilpi **m** *2nd Secretary (Consular Affairs)*
Mr Vesa Kivinen **m** *Counsellor (Police Co-operation)*
Mrs Anu Birgitta Vuorinen **m** *Counsellor (Education & Science)*
Captain (N) Mika Sakari Raunu **m** *Defence Attaché*

FRANCE

Embassy of France
58 Knightsbridge SW1X 7JT
020 7073 1000
Fax 020-7073 1004
www.ambafrance-uk.org

Consular Section
21 Cromwell Road SW7 2EN
020 7073 1200
Fax 020 7073 1201

Visa Section
6A Cromwell Place SW7 2EW
020 7073 1250
Fax 020-7073 1246

Cultural Section
23 Cromwell Road SW7 2EL
020 7073 1300
Fax 020 7073 1326

Science & Technology Section
6 Cromwell Place SW7 2JN
020 7073 1380
Fax 020 7073 1390

Trade Commission – Business France
Brettenham House,
Lancaster place,
London WC2E 7EN

Taxation Section
58 Knightsbridge SW1X 7JT
020 7073 1000
Fax 020 7073 1196

Customs Section
58 Knightsbridge SW1X 7JT
Tel 020 7073 1000
Fax 020 7073 1159

Economic Section
58 Knightsbridge SW1X 7JT
Tel 020 7073 1000
Fax 020 7073 1189

HER EXCELLENCY MRS CATHERINE COLONNA *Ambassador Extraordinary & Plenipotentiary (since 2 September 2019)*
Mr Gerrit Olivier François Van Rossum m *Deputy Head of Mission*
Rear Admiral Hervé Jean-Louis André Hamelin m *Defence Attaché*
Mr Emmanuel Paul Daniel Masse m *Minister-Counsellor (Economic & Financial Affairs)*
Mr Guillaume Bazard m *Consul General*
Mr Guillaume Jean Benoît Lacroix m *First Counsellor*
Mrs Victoire Ract-Madoux m *Press Counsellor*
Mr Nicolas Dasnois *Counsellor (Political)*
Mrs Camille Pintout *Counsellor (Political)*
Mrs Anissia Morel m *Legal Adviser*
Mr Pierre-Jean Albrand *Private Secretary Deputy Press Counsellor*
Mrs Elisabeth Meyer m *Counsellor (Political)*
Mrs Cécile Driesbach *Counsellor*
Mr Bertrand Buchwalter m *Counsellor (Cultural), Director of the Institut Français*
Mr Nicolas Le Van Xieu m *Secretary-General*
Mr Stanislas François Eleuthère Godefroy m *Counsellor (Economic Affairs)*
Mrs Minh-Hà Pham *Counsellor (Science & Technology)*
Mr Romain Djoudi *Attaché (Customs)*
Mrs Estelle Cros m *Counsellor (Judicial Affairs)*
Mr Pierre-Yves Cordier m *Counsellor (Nuclear)*

Mrs Nathalie Skiba m *Counsellor (Police)*
Mr Arnaud Philippe Denis Leretour m *Trade Commissioner*
Mrs Marguerite Moleux m *Counsellor (Social Affairs)*
Mr Thomas Ernoult m *Counsellor (Financial Affairs)*
Mrs Heloise Pestel m *Counsellor (Agriculture)*
Mr Jean-Charles Ledot *Deputy Consul General*
Mrs Julie Poirot m *Deputy Counsellor (Agriculture)*
Captain Julien J L Lalanne de Saint-Quentin m *Naval Attaché*
Colonel Patrick Bryant m *Air Attaché*
Colonel Nicolas Filser m *Military Attaché*
Mr Nicolas Drogi *Attaché (Defence Equipment)*
Mr Edouard Assanelli *1st Secretary*
Mr François Jouffroy m *1st Secretary*
Mr Gaetan Lehuic m *1st Secretary*
Mrs Sohie Marie Anne Zietek m *3rd Secretary (Administrative Affairs)*
Mr Guillaume Maurice Adrien Faivre m *Property Manager*
Mr Robin Lacroix *3rd Secretary*
Mrs Anne Claude Quistrebert Boeffard m *3rd Secretary*
Mr Samuel Chapron m *3rd Secretary*
Mrs Victoria Lenoel *Vice Consul*
Mr Julien Jean Henri Guyot m *Vice Consul*
Mr Dragoslav Zachariev *Deputy Director for Institut Français, Audiovisual Attaché*
Mr Alexandre Auddin *Paymaster (Administrative Affairs)*
Mr Stéphane Harzelec *Cultural Attaché (Administrative Affairs)*
Mr Stéphane Jouvet m *Paymaster*
Mrs Isabelle Manci m *Cultural Attaché*
Mr Rudy Raymond R Ropital m *Attaché (Police)*
Mr Pascal Jean Remi Cornot m *Head of Security*
Mrs Alexandra Barreau-Jouffroy m *Attaché (Taxation)*
Mrs Melanie Alice P Malnou-Diviella m *Deputy Defence Attaché*
Mr François Mercier *Attaché (Police Liaison Officer)*
Mrs Catherine Courbarien *Attaché (Protocol)*
Mr Gautier Houel *Attaché (Economic Affairs)*
Mrs Frederique Lefevre *Commercial Attaché (Business France)*
Mrs Raffaella Silvetti *Attaché (Business France)*
Mrs Mélisande Louise Elise Roche *Inward Investment Director (Business France)*
Mrs Florence Marie ELodie Ferran m *Higher Education and Research Attaché*
Mr Damien Loïc Vialle m *Attaché for Higher Education*
Mrs Vanessa Fines *Cultural Attaché (Administrative Affairs)*
Mrs Krystèle Petris *Attaché*
Mrs Frédérique Moreira m *Vice Consul*
Mr Philippe Colin *Attaché (Police Liaison Officer)*
Mr Bruno Chetanneau *Attaché (Police Liaison Officer)*
Mr Stephane Christophe Foin m *Deputy Cultural Counsellor*
Ms Mathias Rambaud *Cultural Attaché (Book Department)*
Mr Grégory Charles Robert m *Head of the Social Department*
Miss Léa Ambre Auclair *Industry and Transport Attaché*
Mr Etienne Benjamin Genty *Project Manager for Economic Affairs (Business France)*

GABON

Embassy of the Gabonese Republic
27 Elvaston Place SW7 5NL
020 7823 9986
Fax 020-7584 0047
gabonembassyuk@gmail.com
www.gabonembassyuk.co.uk

HER EXCELLENCY MRS AICHATOU SANNI AOUDOU *Ambassador Extraordinary & Plenipotentiary (Since 22 September 2015)*
Miss Wendy Marcelle Bilong *Counsellor (Chancery)*
Mr Lie Patrick Mouvogny m *Counsellor (Communications)*
Mr Willy Hugues Lemambot Mbele *Counsellor (Protocol & Public Relations)*
Mrs Ruth Mouvogny m *2nd Secretary*

THE GAMBIA

The Gambia High Commission
57 Kensington Court W8 5DG
020 3928 9770
Fax 020 7229 9225
gambiahighcomuk@btconnect.com
Monday-Thursday 09.30-17.00, Friday 09.30-13.00

HIS EXCELLENCY MR FRANCIS R BLAIN *High Commissioner (since 21 November 2017)*

Mr. Alieu Njie **m** Charge d'Affaires
Mr. Sulayman S Touray Counsellor
Mr. Abu Bakr Jawara First Secretary
Mr. Ousman Jarjue Finance Attache
Mrs. Mama O. K Jobe Conateh Senior Assistant Protocol

GEORGIA

Embassy of Georgia
20 St George's Square, SW1V 2HP
020 7348 1941
Fax 020 7603 6682
london.emb@mfa.gov.ge
www.uk.mfa.gov.ge

Consular Section
020 7348 1942
london.con@mfa.gov.ge

HER EXCELLENCY MS SOFIO KATSARAVA *Ambassador Extraordinary & Plenipotentiary (Since 14 April 2020)*
Mr George Saganelidze **m** *Minister Plenipotentiary*
General Malkhaz Makaradze **m** *Defence Attaché*
Ms Mary Chakvetadze *Counsellor*
Mr Giorgi Kobakhidze *Counsellor*
Ms Lia Melikishvili *Counsellor*
Mr Paata Papashvili *Consul*
Mrs Ana Nozadze **m** *1st Secretary*

GERMANY

Embassy of the Federal Republic of Germany
23 Belgrave Square, Chesham Place, London, SW1X 8PZ
Phone: 020 7824 1300
Fax: 020 7824 1449
Email: info@lond.diplo.de
Web: www.uk.diplo.de

Passport & Visa Section (by online appointment only)
Fax: 020 7824 1449
Phone Visa Information Service: 020 7824 1466
Phone Passport Information Service: 020 7824 1426

Vacant
Ambassador

Mrs Julia Katharina Gross **m** *Minister (Deputy Head of Mission)*
Brigadier General Michael Oberneyer **m** *Defence Attaché*
Mr Dietrich Jobst Elard Eberhard Edel Lingenthal **m** *Minister (Finance)*
Mr Karl Matthias Klause **m** *Minister (EBRD)*
Mr Darius Rahimi-Laridjani **m** *Minister-Counsellor (Consular)*
Dr Clemens Kohnen * *Minister-Counsellor (Political)*
Mr Markus Knauf **m** *Minister-Counsellor (Economic)*

Mr Thilo Botzenhardt **m** *1st Counsellor (Political)*
Mr Jochen Moeller *1st Counsellor (Press)*
Colonel Stephan Breidenbach **m** *Air Attaché*
Mr André Griese **m** *1st Counsellor (Political)*
Captain (Navy) Wolfgang Heuer **m** *Naval Attaché*
Mr Rainer Sulzer **m** *Counsellor (Economic)*
Mr Julian Frohnecke **m** *Counsellor (Economic)*
Mr Herbert Ernst Ludwig Düll **m** *Counsellor (Social & Labour)*
Ms Svenja Friedrich *Counsellor (Transport)*
Mr Wolfgang Stuetz *Counsellor (Administration)*
Mr Christian Decoster **m** *1st Secretary (Political)*
Ms Britta Schlueter *1st Secretary (Political)*
Lieutnant Colonel Stafan Alves Kraus **m** *Military Attaché*
Mr Erwin Albert Walter Ganzer **m** *1st Secretary (Political)*
Mr Tim Rauschan *1st Secretary (Political)*
Mr Jens Rohrbach **m** *2nd Secretary (Federal Police Liaison)*
Mr Johannes Peter Gerling *2nd Secretary (Finance)*
Mr Gerrit Moerking **m** *2nd Secretary (Administration)*
Mrs Mariko Sara Higuchi **m** *2nd Secretary (Economic)*
Mrs Marlen Sulzer **m** *2nd Secretary (Administration)*
Mrs Petra Troise **m** *2nd Secretary (Administration)*
Mr Michael Hagenburger **m** *2nd Secretary (Consular)*
Mr Wolfgang Rainer Huesgen **m** *2nd Secretary (Consular)*
Mrs Petra Hanefeld **m** *2nd Secretary (Press)*
Ms Lisa Katharina Hemmer *2nd Secretary (Political)*
Ms Theresa von Saldern *2nd Secretary (Cultural)*
Ms Silvia Scharf **m** *2nd Secretary (Administration)*
Mrs Doris Ernst **m** *2nd Secretary (Consular)*
Ms Kerstin Schneider *2nd Secretary (Police Liaison)*
Mr Michael Fuchs **m** *3rd Secretary (Political)*
Mr Thomas Theo Schmitt *3rd Secretary (Security)*
Ms Sarah Hein *3rd Secretary (Political)*
Mr Axel Meyer **m** *3rd Secretary (Police Liaison)*
Mr Matthias Schmitt **m** *3rd Secretary (Customs Liaison)*
Mr Marco Peter Johannes Kensy *Attaché (Security)*
Ms Vanessa Fritsch *Attaché (Security)*
Mr Michael Marx **m** *Attaché (Security Advisor)*
Ms Juliane Dagmar Busch **m** *Attaché (Consular)*
Ms Sophia Elisabeth Hirthammer **m** *Attaché (Political)*
Ms Lilija Amamitch *Attaché (Consular)*
Mr Jan-Gerd Wilken **m** *Chief Petty Officer (Military)*
Mr Marcus Meyer **m** *Attaché (Military)*
Mr Dominik Steimann *Attaché (Consular)*
Mrs Janine Adu **m** *Attaché (Consular)*
Mr Maik Laurin Eisbrenner **m** *Attaché (IT/Administration)*
Mrs Rita Thomas * *Attaché (Security)*
Mr Egon Goebel **m** *Assistant Attaché (Administration)*
Mrs Natalia Schaub **m** *Assistant Attaché (Economic)*
Mrs Andrea Karin Le Bruen **m** *Assistant Attaché (PA Ambassador)*
Mrs Friederike Weber-Rahman **m** *Assistant Attaché (PA Deputy)*
Mr Ricco Langer *Assistant Attaché (Political)*
Ms Jacqueline Heinzelmann *Assistant Attaché (Press)*
Ms Maja von Bodungen *Assistant Attaché (Political)*
Mrs Dagmar Scholze **m** *Assistant Attaché (Administration)*
Mrs Andrea Hanses *Assistant Attaché (Cultural)*
Mrs Marion Coqui **m** *Assistant Attaché (Economic)*
Mrs Anke Elisabeth Schroeder **m** *Assistant Attaché (Consular)*
Mrs Susanne Huesgen **m** *Assistant Attaché (Consular)*
Mr Mirko Roenicke *Assistant Attaché (Military)*
Mr Timo Fiebelkorn **m** *Flight Sergeant*
Mr Thomas Wothe **m** *Assistant Attaché (Administration)*
Mr Christian Biedermann **m** *Assistant Attaché (Political)*
Ms Corinna Schäfer *Assistant Attaché (Consular)*
Mrs Lisa Lewis **m** *Assistant Attaché (Military)*
Mrs Andrea Barbara Thumann **m** *Assistant Attaché (Consular)*
Mrs Aysun Bruckmann-Yazici **m** *Assistant Attaché (Consular)*

Mr Ferdinand Wolfer *Assistant Attaché (Consular)*
Mr Benjamin Veit **m** *Assistant Attaché (Consular)*
Ms Julia Luethje *Assistant Attaché (Administration)*
Ms Pia Willinghoefer *Assistant Attaché (Consular)*
Mr Ihsan Ircal *Assistant Attaché (Administration)*
Mr Wolfgang Reschke **m** *Assistant Attaché (Administration)*
Mr Eyyup Vural **m** *Assistant Attaché (Administration)*

GHANA

High Commission of the Republic of Ghana
13 Belgrave Square SW1X 8PS
020 7201 5900
Fax: 020 7245 9552
Email: gh.donlon@gmail.com; ghmfa31@ghc-uk.org
Website: www.ghanahighcommissionuk.com
Monday-Friday: 09:30-13:00 and 14:00-17:00
Monday-Friday: 09:30-13:00 and 14:00-17:00 (Winter)

Passports, Immigration, Education, Trade & Investment, IMO Affairs and Police Liaison Office
104 Highgate Hill, N6 5HE
020 8342 7501
Email: gh.donlon@gmail.com
Website: www.ghanahighcommissionuk.com
Monday-Friday: 09:30-13:00

HIS EXCELLENCY PAPA OWUSU-ANKOMAH **m** *High Commissioner (From 2017-2020 and 2021 till date)*
        Mrs. Augustina Owusu-Ankomah
Mrs Rita Tani Iddi * *Deputy High Commissioner*
Commodore Eric Adu **m** *(Defence Adviser)*
Group Captain Thomas Niifio Okai **m** *(Deputy Defence Adviser)*
Mr Peprah Ampratwum * *Minister (Head of Chancery)*
Mr Gabriel Owusu Ansah **m** *Minister (Consular & Welfare)*
Ms Afua Gyasiwa Gaisie * *Minister-Counsellor (Education)*
Mrs Josephine Donkor * *Minister-Counsellor (Passport & Immigration)*
Mr Charles Agyeman Attafuah * *Minister-Counsellor (Education)*
Mrs Freda Bediako-Puni **m** *Minister-Counsellor (Commonwealth & Diaspora)*
Mr Papa Kow Bartels * *Minister-Counsellor (Trade & Investment)*
Ms Milana Agyeman * *Minister-Counsellor (Treasury)*
Mr Daniel Darlington Kwaku Aheto * *Counsellor (Protocol/Administration)*
Mr. Dodzie Numekevor **m** *Counsellor (Information & Public Affairs)*
Mr Ransford Kwasi Sarpong * *Counsellor (Treasury)*
Mrs. Joana Nyarko-Mensah Adika * *Counsellor (Political & Economic)*
Mr Samuel Tetteh Mensah **m** *1st Secretary (Finance)*
Mr Alex Ayi Adi **m** *1st Secretary (Treasury)*
Mrs Mabel Larko Adjei **m** *1st Secretary (Treasury)*
Ms Eno B. Appiah-Menka * *1st Secretary (Consular & Welfare)*
Mr Isaac Kwaku Danquah **m** *1st Secretary (Passport & Immigration)*
Ms Barbara Mahama * *1st Secretary (Passport & Immigration)*
Ms Wendy Koshie Bruce Tetteh * *1st Secretary (Consular & Welfare)*
Mrs Theodora Adu Acheampong * *1st Secretary (Passport & Immigration)*
Mrs Gladys Owusu Agyei **m** *2nd Secretary (Administration & Communications)*
Mrs Priscilla Agyenim-Boateng Barnor **m** *2nd Secretary (Administration)*
Ms Nancy Naa Tekwor Nartey * *3rd Secretary (Protocol)*
Mr Solomon Otoo **m** *2nd Secretary (Protocol)*
Mr Edward Tudzi * *3rd Secretary (Finance)*
Mr Prince Nii Lantey Lamptey **m** *3rd Secretary (Passport & Immigration)*
Mr Reuben Romeo Awuni **m** *3rd Secretary (Technical Attaché)*

GREECE

Embassy of Greece

36

1A Holland Park, W11 3TP.
020 7229 3850
gremb.lon@mfa.gr
www.mfa.gr/uk

Economic & Commercial Office
020 7727 8860
ecocom.london@mfa.gr

Defence Attaché's Office
020 7727 3785
London_defatt@navy.mil.gr

Consular Office
020 7313 5600-5609
grcon.lon@mfa.gr

Public Diplomacy Office (Press)
020 7727 3071
pdo.lon@mfa.gr

Maritime Affaires Office
020 7727 0507
hma.london@hcg.g

Police Liaison Office
020 7313 8951
Liaison.officer.uk@astynomia.gr

Educational Affaires Office
020 7221 0093 and 5977
educationofficelondon@gmail.com

HIS EXCELLENCY MR IOANNIS RAPTAKIS **m** *Ambassador Extraordinary & Plenipotentiary*
(since 2 October 2020)
　　　Mrs Georgia Soultanopoulou
　Mrs Iphigenia Kanara **m** *1st Counsellor (Deputy Head of Mission)*
Captain Ioannis Papavlachos **m** *Defence Attaché*
Mr Yerassimos Lazaris *Minister-Counsellor (Economic & Commercial)*
Ms Mariana Garyfallia Varvarrigou *Minister-Counsellor for Press*
Mr Konstantinos Thanopoulos **m** *1st Counsellor (Political)*
Commander Dimitrios Raptis **m** *Maritime Attaché*
Mrs Eleni Soupiana **m** *1st Counsellor (Press & Communication)*
Commander Panagiota Koutra **m** *Alternate Maritime Attachée*
Mrs Georgia Velentza *1st Secretary (Economic & Commercial)*
Ms Aikaterini Tsounakou *1st Secretary (Economic & Commercial)*
Mr Georgios Drakopoulos *2nd Secretary (Political)*
Mr Christos Goulas *3rd Secretary (Political) - Consul*
Police Major Elisavet Toufa *Police Liaison Officer*
Mrs Eirini Veroni **m** *Deputy Counsellor (Education)*
Mrs Eleni Skarveli **m** *Adviser (Director Information & Tourism)*
Mrs Stavroula Metaxa **m** *Secretary for Press*
Mrs Fersa Varouti **m** *Attaché (Consular)*

GRENADA

High Commission for Grenada
The Chapel, Archel Road, West Kensington W14 9QH
020 7385 4415
Fax 020 7381 4807
office@grenada-highcommission.co.uk
www.grenadahclon.co.uk

Monday-Friday 09.00-17.00
Consular Hours : Monday-Friday : 10.00-14.00

HER EXCELLENCY MS LAKISHA ABBA GRANT *High Commissioner (since 7 May 2019)*

Mr Samuel Sandy *Consul*
Ms Xiaowei Chen Diplomatic *Attaché*

GUATEMALA

Embassy of Guatemala
1st Floor & Suite1, 2nd Floor
105a Westbourne Grove W2 4UW
020 7221 1525
embgranbretana@minex.gob.gt - General and Ambassador's Office
adminUK@minex.gob.gt - Administrative

Consular Section
Suite 2, 2nd Floor
105a Westbourne Grove W2 4UW
020 7221 7448
consuladoUK@minex.gob.gt - Consular Section
emergenciasUK@minex.gob.gt - Emergencies

HIS EXCELLENCY MR JOSÉ ALBERTO BRIZ GUTIÉRREZ *Ambassador Extraordinary & Plenipotentiary (since 27 May 2021), Permanent Representative to the International Maritime Organization and to the International Sugar Organization*

Ms Olga Maria Perez Tuna *Minister-Counsellor*
Mr Pedro Gordillo *1st Secretary & Consul*
Ms Demet Maya Basaran Bethancourt *3rd Secretary*

GUINEA

Embassy of the Republic of Guinea
239 Old Marylebone Road, London, NW1 5QT
020 7258 9640/46
Fax
embassyofguinea@gmail.com

His Excellency, Mr Alexandre Cece Loua **m** *Ambassador Extraordinary & Plenipotentiary (since 18 November 2017)*
    Mrs Yeli Yeli Pauline Thealoua
Mr Aly Diallo **m** *(First Secretary in Charge of Economic & Political affaires)*
Mr Diguena Iromou **m** *(First Secretary in charge of Finance)*
Mr Ahmed Sidibe **m** *(Consul)*
Mrs Habibatou Cherif **m** *(Administrative Attaché)*

GUINEA-BISSAU

Embassy of the Republic of Guinea-Bissau
94 Rue St. Lazare 75009 Paris
0033 1 48 74 36 39

Vacant *Ambassador Extraordinary & Plenipotentiary*
Mrs Maria Filomena Embalo Araujo Vieira **m** *Counsellor (Economic)*
Mr José Filipe Fonseca **m** *Counsellor*
Mr Oscar Batica Ferreira **m** *1st Secretary*

GUYANA

High Commission for Guyana
3 Palace Court Bayswater Road W2 4LP
Tel: 020 7229 7684
Fax 020 7727 9809
guyanahc1@btconnect.com
www.guyanahclondon.co.uk

Vacant *High Commissioner*
Ms Vonetta Victor *Counsellor*
Miss Natala Anderson *Second Secretary*

HAITI

Embassy of the Republic of Haiti
21 Bloomsbury Way
London WC1A 2TH
0203 771 1427
Email: info.haitiuk@diplomatie.ht
Office Hours: 9:30 am to 5:00 pm

HIS EXCELLENCY MR EUVRARD SAINT AMAND **m** *Ambassador Extraordinary & Plenipotentiary (since 4 November 2020)*
          Mrs Wilmide Saint Amand
Mr Wadner Arthus *Counsellor*
Ms Anne-Gaelle Lissade **m** *1st Secretary*

HOLY SEE

Apostolic Nunciature
54 Parkside SW19 5NE
020 8944 7189
Fax 020 8947 2494
Monday-Friday 09.00-17.00

HIS EXCELLENCY ARCHBISHOP CLAUDIO GUGEROTTI *Apostolic Nuncio (Sine 1 October 2020)*
Monsignor John John Kallarackal *1st Counsellor*

HONDURAS

Embassy of Honduras
4th Floor 136 Baker Street W1U 6UD
(*Building entrance is on Marylebone Road)
020 7486 4880
Fax 020 7486 4550
hondurasuk@lineone.net
hondurasembassyuk@gmail.com
www.hondurasembassyuk.co.uk
Monday-Friday 9.00-13.00 & 14.00-17.00

HIS EXCELLENCY MR IVAN ROMERO-MARTINEZ **m** *Ambassador Extraordinary & Plenipotentiary (since 22 January 2008)*
          Mrs Mirian Nasser de Romero
Mr Jose Eduardo Atala Midence *Counsellor*

HUNGARY

Embassy of Hungary
35 Eaton Place SW1X 8BY
020 7201 3440
Fax 020 7823 1348

mission.lon@mfa.gov.hu
www.mfa.gov.hu/emb/london
Monday-Thursday 08.30-17.00 & Friday 08.30-14.00

Consular Department
35/B Eaton Place SW1X 8BY
020 7235 5218
Fax 020 7235 8630
konz.lon@mfa.gov.hu
Monday-Friday 09.30-12.00

Economic, Investment & Trade Commission
46 Eaton Place SW1X 8AL
020 7235 8767
Fax 020 7235 4319
trade.london@mfa.gov.hu

Hungarian Cultural Centre
10 Maiden Lane WC2E 7NA
020 7257 2023
Fax 020 7240 4847
info@hungary.org.uk

HIS EXCELLENCY DR FERENC KUMIN m *Ambassador Extraordinary & Plenipotentiary (since 8 May 2020)*
    Mrs Viktória Kumin

Dr Péter Palóczi m *Deputy Head of Mission*
Col Viktor Makay m *Defence Attaché*
LTC Zoltán Tiszai m *Deputy Military Attaché*
Mr Lajos Oláh * *Counsellor (Head of the Consular Section)*
Mr Máté Gábor Vincze m *(Director of The Hungarian Cultural Centre)*
Mr László Péter Orosz *1st Counsellor*
Mrs Viktória Imolyáné Kiss m *2nd Counsellor (Political Affairs)*
Mr Peter Hlinka * *2nd Counsellor (Political Affairs)*
Mr Ga'bor Takács-Carvalho m *1st Secretary (Scientific and Technology Affairs)*
Ms Enikő Magyar *1st Secretary* (Agriculture and Environmental Affairs)
Dr Éva Simon *1st Secretary (Consul)*
Ms Petra Magdolna Hajdu * *1st Secretary*
Mr Levente Gáspár * *1st Secretary (Head of Finance)*
Mr János Bakó m *2nd Secretary (Investment and Trade Affairs)*
Dr Olivér Pál Pintér m *2nd Secretary (Consul)*
Mr Tamás Amer m *2nd Secretary (Investment & Trade)*
Ms Andrea Palotai *2nd Secretary*
Mr Mihály Bóra * *3rd Secretary* (Political Affairs)
Dr Petra Jarosi m *3rd Secretary (Consul)*
Mr László Krisztián Havas *3rd Secretary* (Political Affairs)
Mrs Katalin Oroszi m *Attaché (Cultural)*
Mr Gábor Ferenc Németh *Attaché (Finance Administrator)*
Mr Barnabás Zoltán Szendrodi *Police Liaison Officer*

ICELAND

Embassy of Iceland
2A Hans Street SW1X 0JE
020 7259 3999
Fax 020 7245 9649
london@mfa.is
www.mfa.is/london
Monday-Friday 09.00-16.00

HIS EXCELLENCY MR STURLA SIGURJONSSON m *Ambassador Extraordinary & Plenipotentiary (since 15 November 2020)*
    Mrs Elin Jonsdottir
Mrs Jónsdóttir Jóhanna m *Counsellor*

Ms Thury Bjork Bjorgvinsdottir *Counsellor*
Ms Brynja Jónsdóttir *Attaché*

INDIA

Office of the High Commissioner for India
India House Aldwych WC2B 4NA
020 7836 8484
Fax 020 7836 4331
adm.london@mea.gov.in
www.hcilondon.gov.in

HER EXECELLENCY MS GAITRI ISSAR KUMAR * *High Commissioner (since 22 June 2020)*
    Mr Sachit Kumar
Mr Sujit Ghosh **m** *Deputy High Commissioner*
Mr Vishwesh Negi **m** *Minister (Political, Extradition, Press & Information)*
Mr Samir Kumar Jha **m** *Minister (Public Diplomacy & Consular)*
Mr Manmeet Singh Narang **m** *Minister (Coordination)*
Ms Vinita Mishra **m** *Minister (Audit)*
Mr Amish Tripathi * *Director, The Nehru Centre*
Mr Anil Nautiyal * *Counsellor (Passport & OCI)*
Mr Subhash Ramakrishna Pillai **m** *Counsellor (Consular)*
Mr Prem Kumar Jhell **m** *Counsellor*
Ms Yamuna Sabapathy Vadivelu **m** *Counsellor (Technical Adviser)*
Air Commodore Prashant Mohan **m** *Air Adviser*
Brigadier Vikramjit Singh Gill **m** *Military Attaché*
Commodore Anil Jaggi **m** *Naval Adviser*
Mr Sameer Mehta **m** *1st Secretary (Audit)*
Mr Malsawmthang Keivom **m** *1st Secretary (Political & Extradition)*
Mr Rohitkumar Rameshchandra Vadhwana **m** *1st Secretary (Economic, Press & Information)*
Mr Shitanshu Chaurasiya **m** *1st Secretary (Education, Project & Maintenance)*
Dr Lilly Gunasekar * *1st Secretary (Political & International Organisation)*
Mr Rohan Rajendra Samant **m** *1st Secretary (Political & Immigration)*
Ms Chinghoihkim Keivom **m** *1st Secretary*
Mr Jaspreet Singh Sukhija **m** *1st Secretary (Trade & Economic)*
Mr Sanjay Kumar Sharma * *Deputy Director, The Nehru Centre*
Mr Mahesh Chawla **m** *2nd Secretary (Protocol, RTI & Head of Chancery)*
Mr S.D.K. Menon **m** *2nd Secretary (Projects & Maintenance)*
Mr Sandeep Singh **m** *2nd Secretary (Administration)*
Mr R.K. Duggal **m** *2nd Secretary (Visa)*
Mr Rajbir **m** *2nd Secretary*
Ms Agnes Toppo * *2nd Secretary*
Mr Kuldeep Negi **m** *3rd Secretary (Audit)*
Mr Ranjeet * *3rd Secretary (Audit)*
Mr Sanjay Kumar **m** *Attaché (Coordination)*
Mr Upendra Singh Negi **m** *Attaché (Accounts)*
Mr Arijit Banerjee * *Attaché (Passport)*
Ms Sadhna Vig * *Attaché (Passport)*
Mr Ravi Shankar **m** *Attaché (Political)*
Ms Lhilhing Sitlhou * *Attaché (Commerce)*
Ms Anita Kumari **m** *Attaché (Consular)*
Mr Pankaj Kumar **m** *Attaché (Visa)*
Ms Kamal Arora **m** *Attaché*
Mr Suraj Mal **m** *Attaché*
Mr Vivek Singh **m** *Attaché*
Mr Ravi Ranjan Kumar **m** *Attaché (Audit)*
Mr Sumit Kar **m** *Attaché (Audit)*
Mr Jaipal Singh **m** *Attaché (Audit)*

INDONESIA

Embassy of the Republic of Indonesia
30 Great Peter Street SW1P 2HW

020 7499 7661
Fax 020 7491 4993
kbri@btconnect.com
www.indonesianembassy.org.uk
Monday-Friday 09.00-17.00

Consular Department & Visa Section
020 7499 7661
Fax 020 7491 4993
Consular@indonesianembassy.org.uk
Mon-Thurs 09.30-12.30, Fri-09.30-12.00 (submission of passports/visas/legalisation),
Mon-Fri 14.30-16.00 (collection of passports/visas/legalisation)

HIS EXCELLENCY DR DESRA PERCAYA m *Ambassador Extraordinary and Plenipotentiary*
     Mrs Diana Mawarsari Percaya
Mr Khasan Ashari m *Deputy Chief of Mission*
Mr Riando Sembiring m Counsellor *(Political Affairs)*
Mrs Galuh Indriana Rarasanti *3rd Secretary (Political Affairs)*
Mr Hagus Indaryanto m *1st Secretary (Political Affairs)*
Mr Adi Winarso m *Counsellor (Minister Counsellor)*
Mrs Anggarini Sesotyiningtyas *1st Secretary (Economic Affairs)*
Mrs Indri Ardini Kesuma m *First Secretary (Protocol & Consular Affairs)*
Mr Ari Wibowo m *Attaché (Communication Affairs)*
Mr Hartyo Harkomoyo m *Minister Counsellor (Information & Socio-Cultural Affairs)*
Miss Primada Nur Hudayadi *3rd Secretary (Protocol and Consular Affairs)*
Mrs Juliartha Nugrahaeny Pardede m *1st Secretary (Public Diplomacy, Press & Socio-Cultural Affairs)*
Ms Juliartha Nugrahaeny Pardede *1st Secretary (Information & Socio-Cultural Affairs)*
Mr Muhamad Jaki Nurhasya m *3rd Secretary (Protocol and Consular Affairs)*
Mr Muhamad Jaki Nurhasya 3rd Secretary (Political Affairs)
Mr Dalili Fauzanhasbi Pranowo 3rd Secretary (information & Socio-Cultural Affairs)
Miss Sayu Oka Widani *Counsellor (Protocol and Consular Affairs)*
Mr Dalili Fauzanhasbi Pranowo m 3rd Secretary (Information Affairs)
Mr Muhammad Arif Rokhman m *Attaché (Education & Cultural Affairs)*
Mr Khairul Munadi m *Attaché (Education Affairs)*
Mr Lollan Andy Sutomo Panjaitan m *Transport Attaché*
Mr Mohamad Rizalu Akbar * *Trade Attaché*
Mrs Indah Purbaharjanti m *Attaché (Communication)*

IRAN

Embassy of the Islamic Republic of Iran
16 Prince's Gate SW7 1PT
020 7225 4208-9
Fax: 020 7589 4440
iranemb.lon@mfa.gov.ir
www.london.mfa.ir

Consular Section
50 Kensington Court W8 5DB
020 72253000
Fax: 020 7938 1615
Iranconsulate.lon@mfa.gov.ir

HIS EXCELLENCY MR BAHARVAND MOHSEN * *Ambassador Extraordinary & Plenipotentiary* (since 4 July 2021)
Mr Seyed Mehdi Hosseini Matin m *Minister & Deputy Head of Mission*
Mr Ahmad Shenavaei m *Minister Counsellor (Consul)*
Mr Seyed Noureddin Vahed Pour m *Minister (Consular Affairs)*
Mr Mesbah Ansari Dogaheh m *Minister (Legal & International Affairs)*
Mr Seyed Abdollah Hosseini m *Minister (Financial & Administrative Affairs)*
Mr Ali Matinfar m *Minister (Trade & Economic Affairs)*
Mr Kiumars Javidnia m *Minister Counsellor (Political Affairs)*
Mrs Goudarzi Motlagh Najmeh * *1st Secretary (Consular Affairs)*
Mr. Yousef Emami Ahari m *1st Secretary (Political Affairs)*
Mr Morteza Kazemi Asl m *2nd Secretary (Administrative)*
Mr Mahmoud Maleki m *3rd Secretary (Press & Communications)*

IRAQ

Embassy of the Republic of Iraq
21 Queens Gate SW7 5JE
020 7590 7650
Fax 020 7590 7679
lonemb@mofa.gov.iq
www.mofamission.gov.iq
Monday-Thursday 09.00-16.00
Friday 09.00–15.00

Consular Section
3 Elvaston Place SW7 5QH
020 7590 9220
Fax 020 7590 9226
iraqi_consulate@hotmail.co.uk
Monday-Friday 10.00-13.00

Military Attaché Office
48 Gunnersbury Avenue W5 4HA
020 8752 1314
Fax 020 8896 0356
newiraq2ma@yahoo.com

Cultural Attaché's Office
4 Elvaston Place SW7 5QH
020 7370 2940
Fax 020 7370 2941
office@iraqiculturalattache.org.uk

Commercial Attaché Office
20 Queens Gate, London SW7 5JE
020 7584 6849
uk@iraqcomattache.com

HIS EXCELLENCY MR MOHAMMAD JAAFAR M BAKR HAIDAR AL-SADR m *Ambassador Extraordinary & Plenipotentiary (since 30 October 2019)*
      Mrs Nahida Melhem
Ms Jwan Khioka *Minister Plenipotentiary*
Mr Razaq Mashkoor m *Minister Plenipotentiary*
Mr Mazin Al-Kaabi *Marine Attaché*
Mr Shakir Mahmood Abaw Al-Garash m *Military Attaché*
Mr Ahmed Mohammed Khalid m *Counsellor*
Mr Mohamad Jawad M H Hamid Al- Eshaikar * *Counsellor*
Mr Sufyan Abbas m *Counsellor*
Mr Ghassan Luaibi Mnati Saddawi m *1st Secretary*
Mr Hasan Hadi Talib *1st Secretary*
Mr Atheer Abood Saeed Al-Saedy m *1st Secretary*
Mr Jawhar Hasan M Ameen m *1st Secretary (Consular)*
Mr Yasser Alkadir A Alattif Al-Moayed *1st Secretary (Cultural Section)*
Mr Ammar Abdulhameed Farhan * *1st Secretary*
Mr Bassam Riyadh Aziz Saleh Nema *1st Secretary*
Mr Ahmed Al-Sadr m *1st Secretary*
Miss Sarah Alsayegh *2nd Secretary*
Mrs Wasan Al-Husseini m *3rd Secretary*
Mr Alaa M Ridha M Hasan Najaf m *3rd Secretary (Consular)*
Mr Alauldeen Riyadh Mohammed Al-Nasseri m *3rd Secretary (Media)*
Mr Wisam Faeq Hatem Hasan m *3rd Secretary (Media)*
Mr Mohanad Qasim m *Attaché*
Miss Hana Jawad Kadhem Al-Zubaidi *Commercial Attaché*
Mr Mohammed Al-Hashmi * *Cultural Attaché*
Mr Ali Auday Mousa Al-Khairalla m *Attaché*

Mr Mohammad Zuhair Al-Hiyali **m** *Attaché*
Mr Maher Mishaal Munef *Attaché*

IRELAND

Embassy of Ireland
17 Grosvenor Place SW1X 7HR
020 7235 2171
Fax 020 7201 2515
londonembassymail@dfa.ie
www.embassyofireland.co.uk
Monday-Friday 09.30 - 12.30 – 14.30 -16.30

Passport & Visa Office
114A Cromwell Road SW7 4ES
Passport enquiries 020 7373 4339
Passport Office Monday-Friday 09.30-16.30
Diplomatic Visa Appointment requests to londonvisaoffice@dfa.ie
For Non-Diplomatic Visa applications please see https://www.dfa.ie/irish-embassy/great-britain/our-services/visas/visas-for-ireland/

HIS EXCELLENCY MR ADRIAN O'NEILL **m** *Ambassador Extraordinary & Plenipotentiary (since 30 August 2017)*
     Mrs Aisling O'Neill
Mr Cyril Francis Brennan *Deputy Head of Mission (Foreign Policy)*
Mr Aidan Carrigan **m** *Counsellor (Finance)*
Ms Fiona Flood *Counsellor (Brexit & EU Affairs)*
Mr Patrick Michael Lonergan *Counsellor (Political Affairs)*
Mr Sean Connolly **m** *Counsellor (Agriculture)*
Mr Martin McDermott * *Counsellor (Justice)*
Mr Patrick Rochford **m** *Counsellor (Economic & Trade Affairs)*
Ms Therese Walsh *1st Secretary (Economic & Trade Affairs)*
Mr David Walsh **m** *1st Secretary (Customs & Revenue)*
Mr John O'Sullivan * *1st Secretary (Consular & Administration)*
Ms Isobel O'Connor *1st Secretary (Irish Community & Culture)*
Ms Fionnuala Callanan *1st Secretary (Press & Information)*
Mr Stephen Garry *1st Secretary (Brexit & EU Affairs)*
Mr Cian O'Laoide **m** *1st Secretary (Finance)*
Mr Ciarán Kelleher Byrne *2nd Secretary (Press & Information)*
Mr Raymond Mullen **m** *2nd Secretary (Foreign Policy)*
Ms Marie-Claire Hughes *2nd Secretary (Political Affairs)*
Ms Rachel Ingersoll *2nd Secretary (Irish Community & Culture)*
Ms Rose Gaughan *Attaché (Passport Services)*
Mr Stephen Walsh **m** *Attaché (Visa Services)*
Mr John Freir *Attaché (Consular Services)*
Ms Ursula Cordial **m** *Attaché (Administration)*

ISRAEL

Embassy of Israel
2 Palace Green Kensington W8 4QB
020 7957 9500
Fax 020 7957 9555
www.embassyofisrael.co.uk
Monday-Thursday 08.30-18.00 & Friday 08.45-13.45

Defence Section
2 Palace Green Kensington W8 4QB
020 7957 9530

Consular Section
15a Old Court Place Kensington W8 4QB
020 7957 9516

HER EXCELLENCY MRS TZIPORA HOTOVELY m *Ambassador Extraordinary & Plenipotentiary (since 30 September 2020)*
    Mr Or Hay Alon
Mr Oren Mamorstein m *Minister-Deputy Head of Mission*
Mr Avraham Koren m *Minister -Consul*
Mr Eliahu Levy m *Minister (Administration)*
Mr Ofer Fohrer m *Minister (Commercial Affairs)*
Mrs Daniela Grudsky Ekstein m *Minister-Counsellor*
Mr Gavriel Lidzi Cohen m *Counsellor*
Mrs Efrat Perri m *Counsellor (Public Affairs)*
Mrs Sharon Ehrlich Bershadsky m *1st Secretary (Tourist Affairs)*
Ms Inbar Sela m *1st Secretary (Communications)*
Mr Ohad Rum Zemet m *1st Secretary (Press)*
Ms Jenny Sedov *1st Secretary (Civil Soc Affairs)*
Mr Omri Magen m *1st Secretary*
Mr Rony Aharon Boumfeld m *Defence Attaché*

ITALY

Embassy of Italy
14 Three Kings' Yard, Davies Street, W1K 4EH
020 7312 2200
Fax 020 7312 2230
ambasciata.londra@esteri.it
www.amblondra.esteri.it

Consular Section
Harp House, 83-86 Farringdon Street, EC4A 4BL
020 7936 5900
Fax 020 7583 9425
consolato.londra@esteri.it
www.conslondra.esteri.it

Cultural Section
39 Belgrave Square, SW1X 8NX
020 7235 1461
Fax 020 7235 4618
icilondon@esteri.it
www.icilondon.esteri.it

Defence Section (Military, Naval & Air Attaché's Offices)
7-10 Hobart Place, SW1W 0HH
020 7259 4500
Fax 020 7259 4511
londra.coad4@smd.difesa.it

Financial Section
2 Royal Exchange, EC3V 3DG
020 7606 4201
Fax: 020 7929 0434
london.office@bancaditalia.co.uk

Trade Commission
Sackville House
40 Piccadilly, W1J 0DR
020 7292 3910
Fax: 020 7292 3911
londra@ice.it
www.ice.gov.it

HIS EXCELLENCY MR RAFFAELE TROMBETTA m *Ambassador Extraordinary & Plenipotentiary (since 29 January 2018)*
      Mrs Victoria Jane Mabbs
Mr Alessandro Motta * *Minister & Deputy Head of Mission*
General Enrico Pederzolli m *Defence Attaché*
Mr Marco Villani * *1st Counsellor (Consul General)*
Mr Massimo Carnelos m *1st Counsellor (Economic Affairs)*
Mr Alberto La Bella m *Counsellor (Political Affairs)*
Mr Paolo Mari *Counsellor (Consular and Social Affairs)*
Mrs Aurora Russi m *Counsellor (Cultural and Press Affairs)*
Mr Francesco De Angelis m *1st Secretary (Consul)*
Mr Federico Maria Dimonopoli *1st Secretary*
Mr Diego Solinas m *1st Secretary (Consul)*
Ms Francesca Maria Dell'Apa *1st Secretary*
Lt. Col. Augusto Vizzini m *Deputy Defence Attaché*
Capt. Andrea Conte m *Attaché (Maritime Affairs)*
Colonel Gaetano Senatore m *Attaché (Customs, Excise & Tax Affairs)*
Mr Luca Golzi *Attaché (Police Affairs)*
Prof. Anna Chimenti * *Attaché*
Dr Katia Pizzi m *Attaché (Cultural Affairs – Director)*
Mr Giovanni Sacchi m *Attaché (Trade Commissioner)*
Mr Maurizio Ghirga * *Attaché (Financial Affairs)*
Mr Amado Harakè *Attaché*
Ms Stephanie Mazzola *Attaché*
Mr Adriano Fantinelli * *Attaché*
Mr Paolo Proietti m *Attaché (Administrative Affairs)*
Mr Fabrizio Fusco m *Attaché (Administrative Affairs)*
Mrs Carmela Buonomo m *Attaché (Administrative Affairs)*
Mr Edoardo Ferrara *Attaché (Consular Affairs)*
Mrs Marisa Vivani m *Attaché (Consular Affairs)*
Mrs Caterina Colapietro m *Attaché (Consular Affairs)*
Mrs Giuseppina Bove m *Attaché (Consular Affairs)*
Mr Domenico Pellegrino m *Attaché (Consular Affairs)*
Miss Anna Illiano Attaché *(Consular Affairs)*
Mr Nicola Locatelli *Attaché (Cultural Affairs)*

JAMAICA

Jamaican High Commission
1-2 Prince Consort Road
London
SW7 2BZ
020 7823 9911
Fax 020 7589 5154
jamhigh@jhcuk.com
www.jhcuk.com
Monday-Thursday 10.00-16.00 & Friday 10.00-15.00

Passport & Visa Section
Monday-Friday 10.30-14.00

HIS EXCELLENCY MR SETH GEORGE RAMOCAN, CD m *High Commissioner (since 22 December 2016)*
      Dr. Lola Ramocan
Mrs Patrice Laird-Grant * *Deputy High Commissioner*
Miss Desreine Antonette Taylor *Minister-Counsellor (Diaspora & Consular Affairs)*
Mrs Renee Lloyd m *Counsellor, (Political & Economic Affairs)*
Mrs Karen Sofia Allwood Stewart m *1st Secretary (Finance & Administration)*
Mr Leondrew Campbell m *Attaché (Finance & Administration)*
Mrs Keisha Knight Walker m *Attaché (Administration)*
Mrs. Claudette Barrett Francis m *Attaché (Administration)*
Mr. Laurence Jones m *Attaché (Commercial)*
Mrs. Marcia Evadney Chung-Ying * *Attaché (Consualar Affairs)*

JAPAN

Embassy of Japan
101-104 Piccadilly W1J 7JT
020 7465 6500
Fax 020 7491 9348
Monday-Friday 09.30-18.00
Visa Section 020 7465 6565 Fax 020 7491 9328
Information Section 020 7465 6500 Fax 020 7491 9347
www.uk.emb-japan.go.jp

HIS EXCELLENCY MR HAJIME HAYASHI **m** *Ambassador Extraordinary & Plenipotentiary (since 16 February 2021)*
        Mrs Haruko Hayashi
Mr Hiroshi Matsuura **m** *Envoy Extraordinary & Minister Plenipotentiary*
Mr Minoru Nakamura **m** *Minister (Finance)*
Mr Takeshi Ito * *Minister (Information)*
Mr Jun Miura **m** *Minister (Political)*
Mr Satoshi Katahira **m** *Minister (Economics)*
Mr Kazuhiro kawase **m**   *Minister & Consul General*
Mr Keita Takahashi **m** *Counsellor (Political)*
Mr Hiroki Aoki **m** *Counsellor (Economic)*
Mr Katsuyuki Eino * *Counsellor (Accounts)*
Mr Susumu Tsuda **m** *Counsellor (Consular)*
Ms Sayako Sumomo *Counsellor (Political)*
Mrs Eriko Hirasawa **m** *Counsellor (Economic)*
Mr Hirooki Ohashi **m** *Counsellor (Information)*
Captain Naoki Abe **m** *Counsellor & Defence Attaché*
Mr Hiroshi Baba *Counsellor (Medical)*
Ms Kotono Takasaki **m** *Counsellor (Administration)*
Mr Toshinori Sano **m** *1st Secretary (Information)*
Mr Hironari Nemoto **m** *1st Secretary (Telecommunications)*
Mr Norikazu Tamura * *1st Secretary (Telecommunications)*
Mr Yusuke Hatakeyama **m** *1st Secretary (Political)*
Mr Kazuya Asakawa **m** *1st Secretary (Transport)*
Mr Atsushi Goto **m** *1st Secretary (Economic)*
Mr Hiroaki Tanaka **m** *1st Secretary (Economic)*
Mr Masayuki Otake **m** *1st Secretary (Political)*
Ms Akiko Kawakami * *1st Secretary (Economic)*
Mr Masashi Kitakubo **m** *1st Secretary (Political)*
Mr Yuichi Ishiguro **m** *1st Secretary (Political)*
Mr Eisuke Miyamaru **m** *1st Secretary (Economic)*
Mr Takuya Tanimoto * *1st Secretary (Political)*
Mr Shunsuke Fujisawa **m** *1st Secretary (Political)*
Ms Chika Mashiko *1st Secretary (Information)*
Mr Tomoyuki Fujino **m** *1st Secretary (Political)*
Mr Manabu Ishizuka **m** *1st Secretary (Economic)*
Ms Norie Yaoita **m** *1st Secretary (Administration)*
Mr Naotaka Ozawa **m** *1st Secretary (Finance)*
Mr Hiroyuki Mitsui **m** *1st Secretary (Economic)*
Ms Yumiko Honda **m** *1st Secretary (Economic)*
Ms Mayuko Takamatsu * *1st Secretary (Information)*
Mr Ryutaro Kojima **m** *1st Secretary (Consular)*
Mr Takashi Inoue *1st Secretary (Account)*
Mr Koichi Sakai **m** *1st Secretary (Political)*
Mr Kazuki Sato *2nd Secretary (Consular)*
Mr Toru Oikawa **m** *2nd Secretary (Security)*
Mr Norichika Shido **m** *2nd Secretary (Administration)*
Ms Kaoru Saiki *2nd Secretary (Information)*
Ms Aki Yano *2nd Secretary (Information)*
Mr Megumi Nakahara **m** *2nd Secretary (Security)*
Ms Hanako Hirashima **m** *2nd Secretary (Information)*
Mr Kazuteru Joko **m** *2nd Secretary (Finance)*
Mr Shintaro Yamazaki **m** *2nd Secretary (Consular)*
Mr Masanori Kono *2nd Secretary (Protocol)*
Mr Hiroaki Takano **m** *2nd Secretary (Economic)*
Mr Enderle Shohei Wada *2nd Secretary (Political)*

Mr Toru Tanishima **m** *2nd Secretary (Consular)*
Mr Kazunari Hirano **m** *3rd Secretary (Account)*
Ms Naori Hase *3rd Secretary (Protocol)*
Mr Jun Nakamoto *3rd Secretary (Telecommunications)*
Ms Mizuho Higashi *Attaché (Account)*
Mr Iori Hirashima **m** *Attaché (Telecommunications)*
Ms Yuka Tomizawa *Attaché (Administration/(Information)*
Mr Keigo kimura **m** *Attaché (Administration)*

JORDAN

Embassy of the Hashemite Kingdom of Jordan
6 Upper Phillimore Gardens W8 7HA
020 7937 3685
london@fm.gov.jo
www.jordanembassy.org.uk
Monday-Friday 09:00-16:00

Consular & Visa Section
6 Upper Phillimore Gardens W8 7HA
Monday-Friday 10:00-13:00 & 14:30-16:00

Defence Attaché's Office
16 Upper Phillimore Gardens W8 7HA
020 7937 9611
Fax 020 7937 7505
Monday-Thursday 09:00-15:00, Friday 09:00-12:00

HIS EXCELLENCY MR MANAR M. DABBAS **m** Ambassador Extraordinary & Plenipotentiary (since 16 September 2021)
                    Mrs Muna Ghazi Ahmad Abuhassan
Mr Omar Mohammad Theeb Ababneh **m** *Deputy Head of Mission*
Mr Bela I Mustafa N Abzakh **m** *1st Secretary*
HRH Princess Haya Bint Al Hussein *1st Secretary*
Mrs Rawan Essam Mohammad Al Faqir **m** *2nd Secretary*
Brig Gen Hasan Abdelhamid Fadel Aburumman * *Military, Naval & Air Attaché*
Col Mohammad Jamil Qarqoudeh **m** *Assistant Military Attaché*
Lt Col Taha Ali Khaleel Alathameen * *Procurement Officer*
Lt Col Ra'ed Jaber Alzayadneh **m** *Military Finance Officer*
Lt Col Maher Ali Mustafa Alzghoul **m** *Finance Officer*
Lt Col Ahmed Abdel Latif Atbtoush **m** *Medical Officer*
Major Mamoun Saleh Salem Alnaimat * *Education & Training Officer*

KAZAKHSTAN

Embassy of the Republic of Kazakhstan
Kazakhstan House, 125 Pall Mall, London SW1Y 5EA
Tel: 020 792 51757
Fax 020 7930 8990
Email: London@kazembassy.org.uk; London@mfa.kz
www.mfa.kz/london
Monday-Friday 09.00-13.00 & 14.30-18.30

Consular Section
Tel: 020 7925 7532 *(only on working days between 12:00 & 13:00)*
Emergency Tel: +44(0)7447470570
Fax: 020 7389 0600
Email: consulate@kazembassy.org.uk;
Monday-Friday 09.30-12.30 & 16.00-17.00 *(except Wednesday)*

HIS EXCELLENCY MR ERLAN IDRISSOV m *Ambassador Extraordinary & Plenipotentiary (since 27 February 2017)*
Mr Zhabolat Ussenov *Minister-Counsellor*
Mrs Dana Masalimova *Counsellor (Economic Affairs)*
Mr Bauyrzhan Zharmagambetov *Counsellor*
Mr Yerzhan Ichshanov *Counsellor*
Mr Azamat Kairolda *Counsellor*
Mr Dauren Doszhanov *Counsellor*
Mr Renat Mussin *Counsellor*
Mr Arsen Omarov *Counsellor*
Ms Ainur Nazarymbetova *1st Secretary (Consul)*
Mr Meiram Duyssimbinov *1st Secretary*
Mr Bagdat Akhylbekov *1st Secretary*
Mr Roman Shinkaruk *Assistant Military Attaché*
Mr Nurlan Ismailov *2nd Secretary*
Mrs Kamshat Kumisbay *2nd Secretary*
Mrs Aigerim Seisembayeva *2nd Secretary (Press Secretary)*
Mr Nurmakhambet Smagul *3rd Secretary*
Mr Kairat Nurmolda *3rd Secretary (Vice Consul)*
Ms Shynar Baitukina *Head of Chancery*

KENYA

Kenya High Commission
45 Portland Place
London W1B 1AS
Tel: 0207 636 2371
Fax: 0207 323 1932
www.kenyahighcom.org.uk

HIS EXCELLENCY MR CALEB MANOA ESIPISU m *High Commissioner (since 28 December 2018)*
        Mrs Waithiegeni Kanguru-Esipisu
Mr Joachim Kamere m Deputy Head
Mr Allan Mburu m Minister-Counsellor I
Mr James Kiiru m *1st Counsellor*
Mr Peter Njiru m *2nd Counsellor*
Mr Aden Mohamed m *1st Secretary*
Mr Isaac Wangunyu m *1st Secretary*
Col. Joseph Mokwena m *Defence Adviser*
Mrs Anne Kamau m *Commercial Counsellor*
Mr Evans Kinyanjui m *Immigration Attaché*
Mrs Dorothy Kamwilu m *Education Attaché*
Mrs Alicent Odipo m *Immigration Attaché*
Mr Ayub Munyifwa m *Financial Attaché*

KIRIBATI

London Honorary Consulate (see Honorary Consuls section below)

KOREA (NORTH)

Embassy of the Democratic People's Republic of Korea
73 Gunnersbury Avenue W5 4LP
Tel 020 8992 4965
Monday-Friday 09.00-12.00 & 14.00-17.00
prkinfo@yahoo.com

HIS EXCELLENCY MR IL CHOE m *Ambassador Extraordinary & Plenipotentiary (since 10 November 2016)*
        Mrs Yong Ae Kim
Mr Song Gi Kim m *Minister*

Mr Kwang Min Kim m *Counsellor (Deputy Permanent Representative to IMO)*
Mr Tong IL Ryang m *2nd Secretary*
Mr Ju Hyon Hwang m *3rd Secretary*

KOREA (SOUTH)

Embassy of the Republic of Korea
60 Buckingham Gate SW1E 6AJ
020 7227 5500/2
Fax 020 7227 5503
Website http://gbr.mofa.go.kr
Monday-Friday 09.00-12.00 and 13:30-17.30

Press & information Office
020 7227 5500 (ext. 615)

Consular Section
020 7227 5500 - 7
Monday – Friday 9.00-12.00 and 14:00-16.00

Visa Section
Monday-Friday 10.00-12.00

Korean Cultural Centre
Grand Buildings 1-3 Strand WC2N 5BW
020 7004 2600
Fax 020 7004 2619
www.kccuk.org.uk
Monday-Friday 10.00-18.00 & Saturday 11.00-17.00

HIS EXCELLENCY MR GUNN KIM * *Ambassador Extraordinary & Plenipotentiary (since 20 August 2018)*
Mr Nahmkook Sun m *Minister (Deputy Head of Mission)*
Captain Hyung Kuk Lee m *Defence Attaché*
Mr Jaegeon Kim m *Maritime Attaché*
Mr Dong Joon Chung * *Minister*
Mr Seung Shin Lee m *Minister*
Mr Jae Ho Chun * *Minister-Counsellor (Finance & Economic)*
Mr Jae Hyung Ryoo m *Minister-Counsellor (Maritime)*
Mr Jung Woo Lee * *Minister-Counsellor (Cultural)*
Mr Hyung Chul Park m *Counsellor (Political)*
Mr Jae Lark Park m *Counsellor (Economic)*
Mr Gyeong Hun Yim m *Counsellor*
Mr Sang Bum Cho m *Counsellor (Interior)*
Mr Moongi Choi m *1st Secretary (Science & ICT)*
Ms Sung Eun Kim * *1st Secretary (Press & Information)*
Mr Sung-Hwan Kim * *1st Secretary (Procurement)*
Mr Inkyu Choi m *Police Attaché*
Mr Kee Joon Nam m *1st Secretary*
Mr Sang Min Moon m *1st Secretary*
Mrs Yea Lim Chae m *1st Secretary*
Mr Dongwa Lee m *2nd Secretary*
Mr Jongsoo Lim m *Legislative Attaché*
Ms Minsoo Kang * *1st Secretary*
Mr Sang Hun Seok m *2nd Secretary*
Ms Jisung Yoo m *2nd Secretary*
Mr Seung Oh Yoo m *3rd Secretary*
Mr Jong Ha Kim * *3rd Secretary*
Mr Jiyun Lim m *Maritime Attaché*
Lt. Col.Dongjin Jeong m *Air Attaché*
Mr Hee Seong Ahn m *Attaché (Education)*

KOSOVO (REPUBLIC OF)

Embassy of the Republic of Kosovo

8 John Street WC1N 2ES
Tel: 020 7405 1010
embassy.uk@rks-gov.net
Monday–Friday 09.00–17.00

Consular Section
Tel: 020 7025 0995
consulate.london@rks-gov.net

HIS EXCELLENCY MR ILIR KAPITI **m** *Ambassador Extraordinary & Plenipotentiary (since 31 December 2021)*
        Mrs Eranda Kapiti
Miss Arrita Gjakova *Minister Counsellor, Chargé d'Affaires*
Ms Liridona Hertica **m** *2nd Secretary (Economic Section)*

KUWAIT

Embassy of the State of Kuwait
2 Albert Gate SW1X 7JU
020 7590 3400/3406/3407
Fax 020 7823 1712
Monday-Friday 09.00-16.00

Cultural Office
Hyde Park House 60A Knightsbridge SW1X 7JX
020 7761 8500
Fax 020 7761 8505
https://kcouk.org/ksims/welcome.htm

Kuwait Military Office
Hyde Park House 60A Knightsbridge SW1X 7LF
020 7761 2800/2811
Fax 020 7761 2810/2820

Kuwait Health Office
40 Devonshire Street W1G 7AX
020 7307 1700
Fax 020 7323 2042

Kuwait Investment Office
Wren House 15 Carter Lane EC4V 5EY
020 7606 8080
Fax 020 7332 0755

HIS EXCELLENCY MR KHALED AL-DUWAISAN GCVO **m** *Ambassador Extraordinary & Plenipotentiary (since 29 April 1993)*
        Mrs Dalal Al-Duwaisan
Mr Khaled AlKhulifah *Counsellor*
Mr Zaid AlHarb **m** *1st Secretary*
Mr Abdullah AlWenayyan **m** *2nd Secretary*
Mr Ali AlYahya **m** *3rd Secretary*
Mr Abdulaziz AlThuwaikh *Attaché (Political)*
Mr Fahad AlMudhaf **m** *Attaché*
Mr Ahmad Alfailakawi **m** *Attaché*
Mr Ghazi Almershed *Attaché*
Mr Ahmad AlSaeedi *Attaché*

Mr Meshaal Abuajel **m** *Attaché*
Mr Waleed Alsaeed **m** *Attaché*
Mr Meshari Alasqah **m** *Attaché*
Mr Sultan Alshammari **m** *Attaché*
Brig. Gen. Nayef AlAsker **m** *Military Attaché*
Col Talal AlTurkomani **m** *Military Attaché* (*Assistant Military Attaché*)
 Col Ebraheem AlMershid **m** *Military Attaché* (*Assistant Military Attaché for Finance & Medical Affairs*)
 Col Anwar AlEnezi **m** *Military Attaché* (*Assistant Military Attaché for Training & Technical Affairs*)
 Dr Fawzan AlFares **m** *Attaché* (*Head of Cultural Office*)
Dr Fahad AlMudhaf **m** *Attaché*
Mrs. Sarah Alawadhi **m** *Attaché*
Dr Abdulaziz Ahmad AlRasheed * *Health Attaché* (*Health Attaché for Medical Affairs*)
Dr Bashar Alhashash **m** *Health Attaché*
Mr Nayef Alrashidi **m** *Health Attaché* (*Assistant Health Attaché for Administration*)
Mr Saleh Alateeqi **m** *Financial Attaché* (*Head of the Kuwait Investment Office*)
Mr Mohammed Al Kharafi *Financial Attaché*
Mr Abdulah Al-Shamlan *Financial Attaché*
Mr Fahad AlSahli *Financial Attaché*
Mr Ali Ibraheem AlQadhi *Financial Attaché*
Mr Mohammad Alderbass *Financial Attaché*
Mr Mohammed AlMenaifi *Financial Attaché*
Mr Ahmad Al-Ateeqi *Financial Attaché*
Mr Abdullah AlHadlaq *Financial Attaché*
Mr Abdulatif Adel M.A.H. Alroumi *Financial Attaché*
Mr Hasan Behbehani *Financial Attaché*
Mr Khalifah Hamad Kh H Alasousi **m** *Financial Attaché*
Miss Tala Zalzalah *Financial Attaché*
Mr Meshari Almutairi *Financial Attaché*
Mr Abdulaziz AlJasem **m** *Financial Attaché*
Mr Abdulaziz AlMajed *Financial Attaché* (*Legal Advisor*)
Mr Saud AlAmiri **m** *Financial Attaché* (*Auditor*)
Mr Khalid AlEbraheem *Financial Attaché*
Mr Nasser AlShawa *Financial Attaché*
Mr Khaled AlHuneidi *Financial Attaché*

KYRGYZSTAN

Embassy of the Kyrgyz Republic
Ascot House 119 Crawford Street W1U 6BJ
020 3865 1994
kgembassy.uk@mfa.gov.kg
https://mfa.gov.kg/ru/dm/vb
Monday-Friday 09.00-18.00

Consular Section
020 3865 1994 (ext. 1907)
kyrgyzconsuluk@gmail.com
Monday, Wednesday, Friday 10.00-13.00

Vacant *Ambassador Extraordinary & Plenipotentiary*

Ms Lira Sabyrova *Chargé d'Affaires a.i. & Counsellor*
Mr Batyrbek Kadyrkulov **m** *1st Secretary & Consul*
Mr Aziret Zhaliev **m** *Attaché (Admin & Protocol)*
Ms. Saltanat Baibagyshova *Attaché (Financial Section)*

LAOS

Embassy of the Lao People's Democratic Republic
49 Porchester Terrace W2 3TS
020 7402 3770

Fax 020 7262 1994
laosemblondon@gmail.com

HIS EXECELLENCY MR PHONGSAVANH SISOULATH **m** *Ambassador Extraordinary & Plenipotentiary* (since 13
February 2019)
  Mrs Monekeo Sisoulath
Mr Bounthala Panyavichith **m** *Minister-Counsellor*
Ms Phoumanininh Vilaysouk *2nd Secretary*
 Ms Niphonekham Khammounheuang *3rd Secretary*
Mr Orlasouksavanh Manhorlathai *3rd Secretary*

LATVIA

Embassy of the Republic of Latvia
45 Nottingham Place W1U 5LY
020 756 31 619
Fax 020 7312 0042
embassy.uk@mfa.gov.lv
http://www.mfa.gov.lv/en/london/

Consular Section
The Grove House
248a Marylebone Road
NW1 6JF
020 7725 9212
Fax 020 7312 0042
consulate.uk@mfa.gov.lv

HER EXCELLENCY MRS IVITA BURMISTRE **m** *Ambassador Extraordinary & Plenipotentiary (Since 16 July 2020)*
  Mr Agris Burmistris
Mrs Sanita Ulmane **m** *Counsellor & Deputy Head of Mission*
Ms Māra Fricberga *Counsellor & Head of Consular Section*
Mr Vitālijs Rakstiņš **m** *Counsellor (Defence)*
Mr Ivars Žukovskis **m** *Counsellor (Economic)*
Mrs Ilze Vītuma **m** *2nd Secretary (Visa Officer, Consular Affairs)*
Mrs Solveiga Latkovska **m** *2nd Secretary (Consular Section)*
Mrs Katrīne Ozoliņa - Žukovska **m** *3rd Secretary (Consular Affairs)*
Ms Līga Renkmane *3rd Secretary (Political & Economic)*
Mr Artūrs Saburovs **m** *3rd Secretary (Diaspora & Media Affairs)*
Ms Inga Sergeiceva *3rd Secretary (Consular Affairs)*
Mr Arnis Jermacāns **m** *Senior Desk Officer (Administrative & Financial Affairs)*

LEBANON

Embassy of Lebanon
21 Kensington Palace Gardens W8 4QN
020 7727 6696/7792 7856
Fax 020 7243 1699
emb.leb@btinternet.com

Consular Section
15 Palace Gardens Mews W8 4RB
020 7229 7265

HIS EXCELLENCY MR RAMI MORTADA **m** *Ambassador Extraordinary & Plenipotentiary (since 9 November 2017)*
  Mrs Jamal Yehia
Mr Marwan Francis **m** *Counsellor (Deputy Head of Mission)*
Miss Rasha Haddad * *1st Secretary*
Miss Oula Khodr * *1st Secretary*
Mr Ralph Nehme **m** *Economic Attaché*

LESOTHO

High Commission of the Kingdom of Lesotho
7 Chesham Place Belgravia SW1X 8HN
020 7235 5686
Fax 020 7235 5023
hicom@lesotholondon.org.uk
lesotholondon@gmail.com
www.lesotholondon.org.uk
Monday-Friday 09.00-16.00

Vacant *High Commissioner*
Ms Lineo Alphoncinah Palime *Counsellor*
Mr Nkopane Thabane *1st Secretary*
Mrs Mantolo Motloheloa **m** *3rd Secretary*

LIBERIA

Embassy of the Republic of Liberia
23 Fitzroy Square W1T 6EW
020 7388 5489
Fax 020 7388 2899
info@embassyofliberia.org.uk
www.embassyofliberia.org.uk
Monday-Friday 10:30-17:00 Spring-Autumn (Chancery closed at 16:30 during winter months)

HER EXCELLENCY MRS GURLY T. GIBSON **m** *Ambassador Extraordinary & Plenipotentiary (since 6 February 2019)*
         Mr Harald Dieter Schwarz
Ms Marian F. Sandi **m** *Minister-Counsellor*
Mr Albert Kjlatoe Jaja **m** *Minister-Counsellor*
Ms Winifred Y Nelson-Gaye **m** *Attaché*
Mr Harry Conway **m** *Policy Officer and Maritime Attaché*

LIBYA

Embassy of Libya
15 Knightsbridge SW1X 7LY
020 7201 8280
Fax 020 7245 0588
Telex 266767
Monday-Friday 09.30-15.30

Consular Section
61-62 Ennismore Gardens SW7 1NH
020 7589 6120
Fax 020 7589 6087

Academic Unit
61-62 Ennismore Gardens SW7 1NH
020 7581 2393

Press Office
15 Knightsbridge SW1X 7LY
020 7201 8280
Fax 020 7245 0588

Vacant *Ambassador Extraordinary & Plenipotentiary*

Mr Ahmed Rmalli **m** *Minister Plenipotentiary*
Mr Khalifa Abubdieda **m** *Minister Plenipotentiary*
Mr Salaheddin Abuaboud **m** *Minister Plenipotentiary*

Miss Samira Ben Ategh *Minister Plenipotentiary*
Mr Esam Matous **m** *Counsellor (Administration)*
Mr Wahid Elhenshiri **m** *Consular Counsellor*
Mr Fouzi Naser **m** *Counsellor*
Mr Ehab Tibar **m** *Counsellor*
Mr Jamaleddin Makaf **m** *Counsellor*
Mr Faiz Elagielli **m** *1st Secretary*
Mrs Enas Kaal **m** *1st Secretary*
Mr Mohamed Elhamdi **m** *1st Secretary*
Mr Mohammed A B Mohammed **m** *2nd Secretary*
Mr Elsidieg Elzawawi *3rd Secretary*
Mr Walid Matough *3rd Secretary*
Mr Ali Elkarom **m** *Defence Attaché*
Mr Aimin Omran **m** Academic Attaché
Mr Basher Drirah *Cultural Attaché*
Mrs Fatma Aletawi **m** *Legal Attaché*

LITHUANIA

Embassy of the Republic of Lithuania
Lithuania House 2 Bessborough Gardens SW1V 2JE
020 7592 2840
Fax 020 7592 2864
amb.uk@urm.lt
http://uk.mfa.lt

Commercial Attaché's Office
020 7592 2862
Fax 020 7592 2864

Consular Section
Monday 13.00-17.00, Tuesday-Friday 9.00-13.00

Visa Section
Tuesday, Wednesday & Thursday 15.00-16.00

HIS EXCELLENCY MR RENATAS NORKUS **m** *Ambassador Extraordinary & Plenipotentiary (since 18 August 2017)*
        Mrs Sandra Smaidryte
Mr Ramūnas Davidonis * *Minister Counsellor*
Mrs Erika Griesiuviene **m** *Counsellor (Consular Affairs)*
Dr Birutė Kunigėlytė-Ziukienė **m** *1st Secretary (Consular)*
Miss Kristina Nepaite *1st Secretary (Consular Affairs)*
Mr Andrius Visockis **m** *2nd Secretary (Consular Affairs)*
Mr Tadas Kubilius * *2nd Secretary (Political)*
Ms Ingrida Darašaitė 1st Secretary (Economic affairs)
Ms Gitana Šukaitytė **m** 2nd Secretary (Political)
Ms Aurelija Šakenytė-Žilinskė **m** *Attaché (consular affairs)*
Mr Rimantas Zaleckis Chief Officer
Colonel Devis Martusevičius **m** *Defence Attaché*
Mr Linas Pernavas * *Police Attaché*
Dr Ula Marija Tornau **m** *Cultural Attaché*
Ms Donata Mauricaitė *Commercial Attaché*
Ms Jolita Lancinskiene *Chief Officer (Finance & Administration)*

LUXEMBOURG

Embassy of Luxembourg
27 Wilton Crescent SW1X 8SD
020 7235 6961
Fax 020 7235 9734
londres.amb@mae.etat.lu

Monday-Friday 09.00-17.00

Consular Section
Visa Office Monday-Friday 10.00-11.45

HIS EXCELLENCY MR JEAN ALFRED OLINGER m *Ambassador Extraordinary & Plenipotentiary (since 16 August 2017)*
        Mrs Véronique Olinger-Masquelin
Mr Jean-Marie Frentz m *Deputy Head of Mission*
Ms Sylvie Gilberte Muschang *1st Secretary (Chancellor)*
Mr Christophe Tommy Zeeb-Ichter *Counsellor (Legal & Financial Affairs)*
Mr Christophe Joseph Serge Brighi *Attaché (Economic & Commercial)*

MADAGASCAR

Embassy of the Republic of Madagascar
5th Floor, One Knightsbridge Green SW1X 7NE
020 7052 8277
ambamad.contact@madagascarembassy.org.uk

Vacant *Ambassador Extraordinary & Plenipotentiary*

Mr Tojonirina Ramarolahy *1st Counsellor and Chargé d'Affaires a.i.*
Mrs Anjaniaina Olivia Rakotonirina m *Counsellor*
Mr Maminarivo Andrianatoandro m *Administrative & Consular Attaché*

MALAWI

High Commission of the Republic of Malawi
36 John Street WC1N 2AT
020 7421 6010
Fax 020 7831 9273
London@malawihighcommission.co.uk
www.malawihighcommission.co.uk
Monday-Friday 09.30-13.00 & 14.00-17.00

HIS EXCELLENCY DR THOMAS JOHN BISIKA m *High Commissioner (Since 27 October 2021)*
        Mrs Chawona Gwendolyn Bisika
Justice Thokozani Agnes Patemba m *Deputy High Commissioner*
Dr Elias Elias Tsokalida m *Counsellor*
Colonel Bernard Patrick Bwanaope m *Defence Attaché*
Mr Maclloyd Basil Kaliza Chapatali m *1st Secretary (Finance)*
Ms Violet Rebecca Chakwera m *Investment Attaché*
Mrs Towera Zimba Mmodzi m *1st Secretary (Admin & Diaspora)*
Mrs Martha Sanyala Gonondo m *1st Secretary (Consular)*
Mr Kondwani Munthali *2nd Secretary (Press & Protocol)*

MALAYSIA

Malaysian High Commission
45-46 Belgrave Square SW1X 8QT
020 7235 8033
mwlondon@kln.gov.my
Monday-Friday: 09:00-17:00

Visa/Passport : Monday-Friday 09:00-12:00;
Consular : Tuesday -Thursday 09:00-12:00
(Covid Alert : Please note that from 9 May 2020 the Immigration and Consular Service Counter are temporarily operating on an appointment basis only)

Administration
0203 931 6180/6181/6198

Protocol
0203 931 6176/6206/6207

Consular
0203 931 6180/6951/6197

Immigration
0203 931 6185/6186/6191

Defence
0203 931 6166/6170/6172/6175

Police Liaison
0203 931 6171/6174

Economic
020 7499 4644 (Trade)
020 7493 0616 (Investment)

Education/Students
020 7985 1252

Tourism
0207 930 7932

Maritime
020 3931 6167/6203

HIS EXCELLENCY MR. ZAKRI JAAFAR m *High Commissioner (since 5 August 2021)*
        Ms. Nor Aini Abdul Rahman
Mr Zahid Rastam m *Deputy High Commissioner/Minister*
Mr Mohd Rozaimi Harun m *Minister (Political)*
Brig. Gen. Safwan @ Asri Ismail m *Defence Adviser*
Ms Rashidah Othman m *Minister Counsellor (Investment)*
Associate Prof. Dr Shafie Mohamed Zabri m *Minister-Counsellor (Education)*
Mr Mohamad Fairoz Rozali * *Attaché (Maritime)*
Ms Qairunnisa Md Alias *Counsellor (Multilateral)*
Mr Mohd Azmi Mohd Ali m *Counsellor (Political)*
ACP Mohamed Alex Imran Abdullah m *Counsellor (Police Liaison)*
Mr Mohd Sayuti Shaari m *Attaché (Immigration)*
Mr Megat Iskandar Ahmad Dassilah m *Counsellor (Commercial)*
Mr Khairil Azwan Abu Mansor m *Counsellor (Education)*
Mr Rohizal Mohd Radzi m *Counsellor (Education)*
Mr Lukman Zulkifly m *Attaché (Education)*
DSP Allen Mohd Salleh m *1st Secretary (Police Liaison)*
Mr Rais Shaari m *1st Secretary (Education)*
Ms Nor Faizah Ismail m *1st Secretary (Commercial)*
Mr Ahmad Fadhlizil Ikhram Abdullah m *2nd Secretary (Bilateral Affairs)*
Major Hairulnizam Baharuddin m *Assistant Defence Adviser*
Mr Muhammad Azrul Mohamed Aker m *Attaché (Education)*
Mr. Izzat Baihaqi Abu Bakar m *Assistant Attaché (Maritime)*
Mr Mohd Fazle Ismail m *2nd Secretary (Administration & Consular)*
Mr Samzah Jamirin m *2nd Secretary (Protocol)*
Ms Sofiah Othman m *2nd Secretary (Finance)*

MALDIVES

High Commission of the Republic of Maldives
22 Nottingham Place W1U 5NJ
020 7224 2135
Fax 020 7224 2157
info@maldiveshighcommission.uk
www.maldiveshighcommission.uk
Monday-Friday 09.30-16.30

HER EXCELLENCY DR FARAHANAZ FAIZAL m *High Commissioner (since 1 February 2020, Ambassador Extraordinary & Plenipotentiary between 18 May 2019 and 31 January 2020)*
     Dr Mohamed Ahmed Didi
Mr Naushad Waheed Hassan Manik m *Deputy High Commissioner*
Mr Mohamed Nazeer m *Minister (Trade Representative)*
L Col Hussain Fairoosh m *Defence Advisor*
Mr Moosa Yameen Shahid m *Counsellor*
Ms Maryam Fathika Fayaz *2nd Secretary*
Ms Aminath Nahee m *2nd Secretary*
Ms Mariyam Afnaan m *3rd Secretary*

MALI

Embassy of the Republic of Mali
Avenue Molière 487 1050 Brussels BELGIUM
00 322 345 74-32
Fax 00 322 344 57 00

Vacant *Ambassador Extraordinary & Plenipotentiary*

Mr Mamounou Toure m *Counsellor*

MALTA

Malta High Commission
Malta House 36-38 Piccadilly W1J OLE
020 7292 4800
Fax 020 7734 1831
maltahighcommission.london@gov.mt
www.foreign.gov.mt
Monday-Friday 09.00-13.00 & 14.00-17.00

High Commissioner's Office and Secretariat
020 7292 4827

Political Section
020 7292 4825

Trade Section
020 7292 4815

Commonwealth Section
020 7292 4811

Public Affairs
020 7292 4811

Culture and Education Section
020 7292 4811

Consular/Information/Citizenship Section
020 7292 4806
Citizenship.london@gov.mt

Visa Section
020 7292 4818
Visa.london@gov.mt

Passport Section
020 7292 4821

Medical Section
020 7292 4829
Medical.london@gov.mt

H.E. Emmanuel Mallia **m** *High Commissioner*
Dr Daniel John Attard **m** *Deputy High Commissioner*
Mr Christian Vella Masini **m** *Second Secretary - Consular*
Dr Michaela Muscat *Maritime Attaché*
Mr Peter Paul Meli *Economic Attaché*

MAURITANIA

Embassy of the Islamic Republic of Mauritania
PO Box 77339, London, W5 9TN
embassymauritania.london@gmail.com
020 7233 6158

HIS EXCELLENCY MR SIDYA EL HADJ * *Ambassador Extraordinary & Plenipotentiary (Since 7 September 2020)*
Dr Ely Sneiba *1st Counsellor*
Mr Abdoulaye Sall * *2nd Counsellor*
Mr Sidaty Toulba * *2nd Counsellor*

MAURITIUS

Mauritius High Commission
32/33 Elvaston Place SW7 5NW
020 7581 0294
Fax 020 7823 8437 / 020 7584 9859
londonhc@govmu.org
londonconsul@govmu.org (consular matters only)
Monday-Friday 09.30-13.00 & 14.00-17.00

HIS EXCELLENCY MR GIRISH NUNKOO **m** *High Commissioner (since 09 August 2015)*
        Mrs Bibi Qamarara Nunkoo
Mr Thailesh Kumar Chamane **m** *Minister Counsellor/Deputy High Commissioner*
Mr Dooshant Kumar Bucktowar **m** *2nd Secretary*
Mr Uttamsingh Goodur **m** *2nd Secretary*
Ms Disha Ragoonath Ragnuth **m** *2nd Secretary*

MEXICO

Embassy of Mexico
16 St. George Street, London, W1S 1FD
Switchboard: 020 7499 8586
E-Mail: mexuk@sre.gob.mx
Web Page: http://www.sre.gob.mx/reinounido
Monday-Friday 09.00-13.00 & 14.00-15.00

Consular Section
16 St. George Street, London, W1S 1FD
consulmexuk@sre.gob.mx

Military & Air Section
8 Halkin Street, London, SW1X 7DW
Tel & Fax: 020 7235 7898

Naval Affairs Section
8 Halkin Street, London, SW1X 7DW
Tel & Fax : 020 7235 6211

Maritime Affairs Section
8 Halkin Street, London, SW1X 7DW
Tel : 020 7235 8475

HER EXCELLENCY MS JOSEFA GONZALEZ BLANCO ORTIZ MENA *Ambassador Extraordinary & Plenipotentiary (since 15 April 2021)*
Ms Yanerit Cristina Morgan Sotomayor **m** *Deputy Head of Mission*
Mrs Norma Salome Munguia Aldaraca **m** *Minister (Multilateral Affairs)*
Mr David Navarro Lara **m** *Military and Air Attaché*
Captain Ramon Vazquez Azpiri **m** *Naval Attaché*
Captain Ramon Lopez Chavez **m** *Deputy Navel Attaché*
Mr Adrian Esteban Santos Ruiz * *Counsellor (Press Affairs)*
Mr Luis Fernando Gutierrez Champion * *Counsellor (Ambassador's Chief Officer)*
Mrs Mónica Sigss Palladares *Counsellor (Scientific and Cooperation Affairs)*
Mrs Aida Guillermina Velasco Perez *1st Secretary (Head of the Consular Mission)b*
Mr Melendrez Armada Rodrigo **m** *2nd Secretary (Tourism Affairs)*
Mr Octavio Perales Sanchez **m** *2nd Secretary (Political Affairs)*
Ms Mariana Herrera Salcedo Serrano *3rd Secretary (Economic Affairs Attaché)*
Ms Stephanie Marie Black León *3rd Secretary (Cultural Attaché)*
Mrs Erika Pardo Rodriguez, **m** *Administrative Attaché*
Mr Antonio Hernández Baca **m** *Vice Consul (Deputy Head of Consular Mission)*
Rear Admiral Jesus Lopez Vallejo **m** *Permanente Alternative Representative to the IMO*
Captain Mauricio Cruz Reyes **m** *Permanente Alternative Representative to the IMO*
Captain Gabriel Fuente Lizarraga **m** *Deputy Naval Attaché*
Mr Oscar Díaz Carmona **m** *First Sergeant*

MOLDOVA

Embassy of the Republic of Moldova
5 Dolphin Square Edensor Road W4 2ST
020 8995 6818
020 8995 6927
embassy.london@mfa.gov.md
www.regatulunit.mfa.gov.md
Monday-Friday 08.00-13.00 & 14.00-17.00

Consular & Visa section
020 8996 0546
consul.london@mfa.gov.md
Monday-Friday 08.00-13.00 & 14.00-17.00

HER EXCELLENCY MRS ANGELA PONOMARIOV **m** *Ambassador Extraordinary & Plenipotentiary (since 28 September 2018)*
        Mr Stefan Martin Christian Kesseleökeöi Majthényi Báró
Mrs Oxana Borta **m** *Counsellor*
Mr Ion Panfil **m** *1st Secretary (Consular Affairs)*
Mrs Laura Banealite **m** *1st Secretary*

MONACO

Embassy of the Principality of Monaco
7 Upper Grosvenor Street London W1K 2LX
0207 318 1081
Fax 0207 493 4563
www. embassy-to-uk.gouv.mc/en
embassy.uk@gouv.mc

HER EXCELLENCY MRS EVELYNE GENTA *Ambassador Extraordinary & Plenipotentiary (since 12 January 2010)*

MONGOLIA

Embassy of Mongolia
7-8 Kensington Court
London W8 5DL
Tel: 020 7937 0150
E-mail: chancery@embassyofmongolia.co.uk
Website: www.embassyofmongolia.co.uk

HIS EXCELLENCY MR ENKHSUKH BATTUMUR **m** *Ambassador Extraordinary & Plenipotentiary (since 28 November 2021)*
    Ms Ganchimeg Purevdorj
Mr Ganbold Gankhuyag **m** *Deputy Head of Mission, Minister-Counsellor*
Mr Zorigtbat Tseveenjav **m** *Counsellor (Trade & Economic Affairs, IMO)*
Ms Enkhtuya Ganzorig **m** *1st Secretary (Consular Affairs, Visa)*
Ms Oyunjargal Ulziitogtokh *2nd Secretary (Education & Cultural Affairs)*
Mr Munkhtushig Bayarbat **m** *Attaché (Protocol)*

MONTENEGRO

Embassy of Montenegro
47 De Vere Gardens, London, W8 5AW
020 3302 7227
Fax 020 3302 7227
unitedkingdom@mfa.gov.me

Vacant *Ambassador Extraordinary & Plenipotentiary*
Ms Natasa Jovovic **m** *Chargé d'Affaires, Minister Counsellor*
Mr Perko Mijatovic *2nd Secretary*
Mr Milan Bigovic * *Defence Attaché*

MOROCCO

Embassy of the Kingdom of Morocco
6 Grosvenor Gardens, London, SW1W 0DH
Tel: 0207 2590382,
Fax 0207 225 38 62
ambalondres@maec.gov.ma
www.morocanembassylondon.org.uk
Monday-Friday 09.00-17.00

Consular Section
Diamond House: 97/99 Praed Street, Paddington, W2 1NT
Tel: 0207 724 07 19/0207 724 06 24
Fax: 0207 7067407
Consmorocco.uk@lycos.co.uk

HIS EXCELLENCY MR Hakim HAJOUI **m** Ambassador *Extraordinary & Plenipotentiary (since 14 December 2021)*
    Mrs Lamia AMOR
Mr Mouaad IBRIZ **m** Deputy *Head of Mission*
Mr Abdelkader Dini **m** *Military, Naval & Air Attaché*
Mr Chakir El Eissaoui **m** *Deputy Military, Naval & Air Attaché & Representative to the IMO*
Mr Brahim Outti **m** *Minister Plenipotentiary*
Mr Khalid El Moujaddidi **m** *Consul General*
Miss Hanane Maoulainine **m** *Counsellor (IMO)*
Mr Salima El Fadili **m** *Counsellor(Economic Affairs)*
Mr Najib Essadki **m** *Counsellor (Political Affairs)*
Mrs Machichi Siham **m** *1ˢᵗ Secretary (Press Affairs)*
Mr Marouan Abousif **m** *1st Secretary (Economic Affairs)*
Miss Myriam Sekkouri Alaoui * *1st Secretary (Cultural Affairs)*
Mr Abderrafi Bensaid * *Vice Consul*

Mr Ahmed Biyoud m *Vice Consul*
Mr Mohamed Ikij m *Vice Consul*
Mrs Houda Bouziane m Consular *Attaché*
Ms Fatna Razouk * *Consular Attaché*
Ms Sanae Ougaddoum * *Attaché*
Mr Tissir Es-Sadraty m Attaché
Mr Mohamed Ma Elainine m *Attaché*
Mr Taoufiq Benhajjou m *Security Attaché*
Mr Jamal El Achaoui m *Security Attaché*

MOZAMBIQUE

High Commission for the Republic of Mozambique
21 Fitzroy Square W1T 6EL
020 7383 3800
sectorconsular@mozambiquehc.co.uk
www.mozambiquehighcommission.org.uk
Monday-Friday 09.30-13.00 & 14.00-17.00
Consular Section: Monday-Friday 09.30-13.00; Inquiries by telephone: Monday-Friday 14.30-16.30

HER EXCELLENCY MS ALBERTINA MARIA DOMINGOS MAC DONALD *High Commissioner (Since 22 April 2021)*
Mr Fulgêncio Timóteo Muchanga * *1st Secretary*
Mr Aurélio Machimbene Matavele Júnior m *1st Secretary*
Mr Fulgêncio Timóteo Muchanga Madinga *1st Secretary*
Ms Margarida Helena Adamo *Financial & Administrative Attaché*

MYANMAR

Embassy of the Republic of the Union of Myanmar
19A Charles Street W1J 5DX
General Office 020 7148 0740
Ambassador's Office 020 7148 0749
Consular Section 020 71480740
Political, Trade, Press & Cultural Affairs Section 020 71480741
Fax 020 7490 7043
admin@londonmyanmarembassy.com
mingalarpar@londonmyanmarembassy.com
consular@londonmyanmarembassy.com
www.londonmyanmarembassy.com

Vacant *Ambassador Extraordinary & Plenipotentiary*
Mr Htun Aung Kyaw * Chargé d' Affaires a.i. and *Minister*
Dr Chit Win m *Minister-Counsellor*
Captain (Navy) Soe Aung m *Defence Attaché*
Mr Kyaw Myint m *1st Secretary*
Mrs Sandar Win Shwe m *2nd Secretary*
Mr Hein Htet Swam *2nd Secretary*
Miss Kyi Thar Thant *2nd Secretary*
Mr Ye Lin Aung m *3rd Secretary*
Mrs Thin Thin Swe m *Attaché*
Ms Ei Myat Mon *Attaché*
Mrs Aye Mya Thawtar m *Attaché*
Mr Han Myo Lwin m *Attaché*
Mr Aung Naing Saw m *Attaché*
Mr Aung Thet Htwe m *Attaché*
Mr Min Min Htike m *Attaché*

NAMIBIA

High Commission for the Republic of Namibia
6 Chandos Street W1G 9LU

020 7636 6244
info@namibiahc.org.uk
Monday to Friday 09.00-13.00 & 14.00-17.00

HER EXCELLENCY MS LINDA ANNE SCOTT *High Commissioner (since 19 December 2018)*
Mr O'Brien Simasiku *1st Secretary (Political & Commonwealth)*
Mr Henry Zamuee **m** *2nd Secretary (Finance & Administration) (Non-Resident)*
Mrs Sarah Haufiku **m** *3rd Secretary*

NAURU

London Honorary Consulate (see Honorary Consuls section below)

NEPAL

Embassy of Nepal
12A Kensington Palace Gardens W8 4QU
020 7229 1594/6231/7243 7853
Fax 020 7792 9861
eon@nepembassy.org.uk
www.uk.nepalembassy.gov.np
Monday-Friday 09.00-13.00 & 14.00-17.00

Vacant *Ambassador Extraordinary & Plenipotentiary*
Mrs Roshan Khanal **m** *Counsellor & Deputy Chief of Mission*
Col. Ratna Bahadur Godhar **m** *Military Attaché*
Mr Ram Babu Nepal **m** *2nd Secretary*
Mr Gajendra Rai **m** *Attaché*
Mrs Pujan Panday **m** *Attaché*

NETHERLANDS

Embassy of the Kingdom of the Netherlands
38 Hyde Park Gate SW7 5DP
020 7590 3200
LON@minbuza.nl
https://www.netherlandsworldwide.nl/countries/united-kingdom
Monday-Friday 09.00-17.00

Ambassador's Office
020 7590 3299
Fax 020 7590 3262

Political Department
020 7590 3294
Fax 020 7590 3262

Economic Department
020 7590 3259

Press, Public Diplomacy & Cultural Department
020 7590 3269

Operational Management Department
020 7590 3252

Consular Department
020 7590 3200

Defence Attaché's Office
020 7590 3244

Army Attaché's Office
020 7590 3244

Agricultural, Nature & Food Quality Department
020 7590 3279

Netherlands Foreign Investment Agency
020 7590 3286

HIS EXCELLENCY MR KAREL VAN OOSTEROM m *Ambassador Extraordinary & Plenipotentiary (since 21 August 2020)*
    Mrs Anna Niessen
Mr Hanno Würzner m *Minister Plenipotentiary*
Mrs Maartje Maria Noordam m *Counsellor (Political Affairs)*
Mr Ivar Nijhuis m *Counsellor (Security and Justice)*
Mr Job Jan Maarleveld * *First Secretary (Political Affairs)*
Mr Rutger Fransen m *2nd Secretary (Political Affairs)*
Mr Dimitri Vogelaar * *Counsellor (Economic Affairs)*
Mr Albert Derk Jan Beltman m *First Secretary (Economic Affairs)*
Mr Roy Spijkerboer *2nd Secretary (Economic Affairs)*
Mrs Daphne Blokhuis m *First Secretary (Infrastructure & Water Management)*
Mr Peter van Tienhoven m *Customs Attaché (Economic Affairs)*
Ms Astrid Suzanne Michelle de Vries *First Secretary (Cultural Affairs and Communications)*
Mrs Johanna Caroline Laura van Voorts Vader m *Attaché (Education and Science)*
Ms Louise Pfältzer *2nd Secretary (Press & Cultural Affairs)*
Mrs Marije Lamaker * *Vice Consul (Consular & General Affairs)*
Captain Gerrit Nijenhuis m *Defence and Naval Attaché*
Lt Colonel Richard Piso m *Military, Air and Deputy Defence Attaché*
Mr Michiel Marchand m *Strategic Liaison Officer (Police)*
Mr Edwin Coppens * *Liaison Officer (Police)*
Mr Chris in het Veld * *Liaison Officer (Police)*
Mr Philippus Jacobus Maria de Jong m *Agriculture Attaché*
Mr Ties Rinze Henk Elzinga m *Counsellor (Netherlands Foreign Investment Agency)*

NEW ZEALAND

New Zealand High Commission
1 Pall Mall East SW1Y 5AU
Monday-Friday 09.00-17.00

Chancery
020 7930 8422
Fax 020 7839 4580
www.mfat.govt.nz/uk
Enquiries: enquiries@nzhc.uk
Consular: consular@nzhc.uk

Defence Staff & Defence Purchasing Office
020 7930 8400
Fax 020 7930 8401

Immigration New Zealand
020 3582 7499 (Visa Application Centre)
Fax 020 7973 0370

Passport Office
020 7968 2730
Fax 020 7968 2739

New Zealand Trade & Enterprise

020 7321 5371
Fax 020 7973 0104

HIS EXCELLENCY MR BEDE CORRY *High Commissioner* (since 2 August 2020)
Ms Shannon Austin m *Deputy High Commissioner*
Brigadier James Bliss m *Defence Adviser & Head New Zealand Defence Staff*
Mr Nicholas Swallow m *Counsellor (Commercial)*
Mr Christopher Page m *Counsellor (Police)*
Mr Chris Kebbell m *Counsellor (Primary Industries)*
Mr Andrew Badrick *Counsellor (Customs)*
Mr Jeremy Palmer *Counsellor (Management) and Consul General*
Mr Benjamin Steele m *Counsellor (Political)*
Ms Katherine Dawson *Counsellor*
Ms Allison King *Counsellor*
Mrs Jasmine Waterworth-Hall m *1st Secretary*
Ms Kate Swan *1st Secretary (Trade & Economic)*
Ms Rosalie Miller *2nd Secretary (Multilateral)*
Mr Aaron Gallen *Attaché*
Commander Tony Masters m *Naval Adviser*
Wing Commander Stephen Thornley *Air Adviser*
Lieutenant Colonel Ian Brandon m *Military Adviser*
Mr Richard John Moore m *Logistics Adviser*
Mr Cedric Blundell m *Business Manager*

NICARAGUA

Embassy of Nicaragua
Suite 2 Vicarage House 58-60 Kensington Church Street W8 4DB
020 7938 2373
Fax 020 7937 0952
embaniclondon@btconnect.com

Consular Section
consulnic.uk@btconnect.com

HER EXCELLENCY GUISELL MORALES-ECHAVERRY *Ambassador Extraordinary & Plenipotentiary (since 15 January 2015)*

NIGER

Embassy of the Republic of Niger
154 Rue de Longchamp 75116 Paris FRANCE
(00) 331 45 04 80 60
Fax (00) 331 45 04 79 73

HIS EXCELLENCY ADO ELHADJI ABOU *Ambassador Extraordinary & Plenipotentiary (Since 5 February 2018)*
Mr Aminou Elh Malam Manzo *1st Counsellor*
Mr Amadou Hassane Mai Dawa *2nd Counsellor*
Mr Ichaou Amadou *1st Secretary*
Mr Aboubacar Alzouma Yandou *1st Secretary*

NIGERIA

High Commission for the Federal Republic of Nigeria
Nigeria House 9 Northumberland Avenue WC2N 5BX
020 7839 1244
Fax 020 7839 8746
Monday-Friday 09.30-17.30
chancery@nigeriahc.org

Immigration Section
9 Northumberland Avenue WC2N 5BX
020 7839 1244
Fax 020 7925 0990
passport@nigeriahc.org.uk
visa@nigeriahc.org.uk
Monday-Friday 10.00-13.00

Defence Section
9 Northumberland Avenue WC2N 5BX
020 7839 1244
Fax 020 7925 1483

HIS EXCELLENCY GEORGE ADESOLA OGUNTADE **m** High Commissioner (since 09 October 2017)
          Mrs. Modupe Oguntade spouse
Deputy High Commissioner (Vacant)
Mr Olukayode Aluko **m** Minister/Head of Information Culture & Sports
Mr Mohammed Shehu Kangiwa **m** Minister (Head of Immigration)
Mr Ahmed Sule **m** Minister/Head (Industry, Trade & Investments)
Mr Ibrahim G.Zanna **m** Minister/Chief of Protocol
Mr Enock N. Gazi **m** Minister/Deputy Head (Information, Culture & Sports)
Mr Basil M. Okolo **m** Minister/Deputy Head of Political
Mr Paulinus Uchenna Nwokoro **m** Minister/Head of Consular, Education and Welfare
Mr Oludare Ezekiel Folowosele **m** Minister/Deputy (Head of Industry, Trade & investment)
Mrs Rose Yakowa-Okoh Counsellor/Head of Chancery
Mr Yekini Abdulrahman-Shola Counsellor
Mrs Suliat A Paramole **m** Counsellor (Political)
Mrs Helen U. Nzeako **m** 1st Secretary (Consular, Education and Welfare)
Mr Henry G. Odunna **m** 1st Secretary (Political/PA to HC)
Mr Adejare Oluwaloseyi **m** First Secretary
Mrs Linda A. Pama **m** 3rd Secretary (Administration)
Mr Wilson Leva Malgwi **m** Third Secretary (Consular, Education and Welfare)
Mr Alfred A. Bamidele **m** Finance Attaché
Mr Azeez I. Obayomi **m** Admin Attaché (OCB/ICT)
Mrs Jane J N Odiachi **m** Admin Attaché (Adminstration)
Mr Yusuf Sule **m** Admin Attaché (Administration)
Mrs Helen E. Taddy **m** Admin Attaché (High Commissioner's Office)
Mr Auwalu Garba **m** Admin Attaché (Administration)
Mrs Cecilia A. Adeoye **m** Admin Attaché (Information, Culture & Sports)
Mrs Mary A. Ushie **m** Immigration Attaché
Mr Mohammed Kaila **m** Deputy Immigration Attaché II
Mr Aliyu Suleiman **m** Deputy Immigration Attaché III
Mr Taiwo A. Hundeyin **m** Deputy Immigration Attaché IV
Mr Bilya Mohammed Mohammed **m** Immigration Attaché V
Mr Ayodeji Olufemi Gbaye **m** Immigration Attaché VI
Brigadier Gen. Abubakar Sadiq Ndalolo **m** Defence Adviser
Navy Captain Mutalib Ibikunle Raji **m** Deputy Defence Adviser (Navy)
Group Captain Fauziyyu Sani Maaji Deputy Defence Adviser (Air)
Lt.Col. Charles C. Odugu **m** Deputy Defence Adviser (Lib)
Maj. Eniola Bankole Oguntuase **m** Deputy Defence Adviser (Finance)
MWO J. Abdul **m** CC/PA- Defence Adviser
Engr. Anas Kawu Suleiman **m** Deputy Alternate Permanent Representative to the IMO
Mr Bwala William Auta **m** Chief Maritime Officer to the Alternate Rep to IMO
Mrs Miedi Aguma **m** Chief Accountant to the Permanent Rep to the IMO
Mr Y M Kankiya **m** Liaison Officer to National University Commission (NUC)

NORTH MACEDONIA

Embassy of the Republic of North Macedonia
Suites 2.1 & 2.2 Second Floor Buckingham Court,
75-83 Buckingham Gate, London SW1E 6PE

020 7976 0535
sek.london@mfa.gov.mk
www.mfa.gov.mk (Ministry of Foreign Affairs)

HER EXCELLENCY MS ALEKSANDRA MIOVSKA *Ambassador Extraordinary & Plenipotentiary (since 5 September 2018)*
Mrs Eli Bojadjieska Ristovski **m** *Minister-Counsellor (Political & Economic)*

NORWAY

Royal Norwegian Embassy
25 Belgrave Square, London, SW1X 8QD
Phone: 020 7591 5500
Fax: 020 7245 6993
emb.london@mfa.no
www.norway.org.uk

HIS EXCELLENCY MR WEGGER CHRISTIAN STRØMMEN **m** *Ambassador Extraordinary & Plenipotentiary (as of the 2nd of January 2019)*
        Reverend Doctor Cecilie Jørgensen Strømmen
Mr Øyvind Hernes **m** *Deputy Head of Mission*
Ms Ragnhild Øverjordet **m** *Counsellor (Administrative & Consular)*
Mr Lars-Erik Hauge **m** *Counsellor (Cultural & Trade)*
Mr Simen Svenheim **m** *Counsellor (Trade, Industry & Fisheries)*
Mr Keith Eikenes **m** *Counsellor (Security & Defence)*
Mrs Kristin Skjefstad Edibe **m** *Consul*
Mr Stein-Ivar Lothe Eide **m** *1st Secretary (Political)*
Mr Audun Skei Fostvedt-Mills **m** *1st Secretary (Political)*
Mr Sigurd Andreas Moe **m** *Police Attaché*
Captain (Navy) Pål Øystein Hope **m** *Defence Attaché*

OMAN

Embassy of the Sultanate of Oman
167 Queens Gate, London SW7 5HE
Switchboard: 020 7225 0001
Fax: 020 7589 2505
E: london2@fm.gov.om
E: london1@fm.gov.om

Information Attaché
020 75843700- 020 75897751
E: info.attache@omanembassy.org

Military Attaché
Tel: 020 7589 0202
PA: 020 7589 0355
E: pa@omanembassy.org.uk

Cultural Attaché
2nd floor, 34 Sackville Street
London W1S 3ED
Tel: 020 78383853
Urgent or out of office hours queries
Cultural Attaché Mobile No: 07503339995
E: m.hadi@omanembassy.org.uk

HIS EXCELLENCY ABDULAZIZ ABDULLAH ZAHIR AL HINAI **m** *Ambassador Extraordinary & Plenipotentiary (since 12 November 2009)*
        Mrs Maryam *Talib Ali Al Hinai*
Mr Issa Saleh Abdullah Saleh Al Shibani **m** *Counsellor - Deputy Head of Mission*
Shaikh Ghassan Ibrahim Shaker **m** minister *Plenipotentiary*
Ibrahim Mohamed Said Al Mardhoof Al Saadi **m** *Minister Plenipotentiary*

Miss Rua Issa Ashraf Al Zadjali - Counsellor
Mr Saud Ali Al Tamtami **m** Counsellor
Mr Mohammed Abdullah Salim Al Zeidi **m** *Counsellor*
Miss Amal Ali Hassan Al Balushi - *1st Secretary*
Mr Zayed Mussallam Jamaan Qatamim Al Mahroon **m** *1st Secretary*
HH Theyazin Haitham Tarik Al Said **m** *Minister Plenipotentiary*
Mr Abdullah Abbas Al Kindi **m** *2nd Secretary*
Mr Saud Mustahail Ahmed Al Mashani **m** *2nd Secretary*
HH Sultan Faisal Turky Mahmmod Al Said -Diplomatic Attaché- Admin
Brigadier Ahmed Ibrahim Salam Ambu Saidi **m** *Military Attaché*
Captain Said Sulaiman Hamed Al Shabibi **m** Ass. Military Attaché
Mrs Abeer Ali Awadh **m** *Cultural Attaché*
Mr Mohammed Khalfan Khamis Al Busaidi **m** *Information Attaché*

PAKISTAN

High Commission for the Islamic Republic of Pakistan
35-36 Lowndes Square SW1X 9JN
020 7664 9276
Fax 020 7664 9224
phclondon@phclondon.org
www.phclondon.org
Monday-Friday 09.30-17.30

Consular Division
34 Lowndes Square SW1X 9JN
Monday-Thursday 10.00-12.30 & Friday 10.00-12.00

HIS EXCELLENCY MR MOAZZAM AHMAD KHAN **m** *High Commissioner (since 14 September 2020)*
    Mrs Leena Salim Moazzam spouse
Dr Faisal Aziz Ahmed **m** *Deputy High Commissioner*
Mr Hassan Ali Zaigham **m** *Counsellor (Political)*
Mrs Rabia Kasuri **m** *Counsellor (Political)*
Mr Muhammad Aneel Zafar **m** *(Counsellor-Head of Chancery)*
Mr Dildar Ali Abro **m** *First Secretary (Political)*
Ms Gullanay Omama **f** *(Consular Affairs)*
Mr Shahnawaz Khan, *Second Secretary (Political)*
Commodore Jamal Alam **m** *Defence & Naval Adviser*
Captain Abid Rafique **m** *Defence Procurement Adviser*
Colonel Rana Muhammad Asif Khan **m** *Army & Air Adviser*
Colonel Muhammed Waqas **m** *Counsellor (PATLO-I)*
Major Wajahat Ali **m** *First Secretary (PATLO-II)*
Mr Asim Gulzar **m** *Minister (Coord)*
Mr Sher Abbas **m** *Counsellor (Coord)*
Mr Faisal Mahmood **m** *First Secretary*
Mr Irfan Tariq **m** *First Secretary*
Mr Nazar Hussain **m** *Technical Attaché*
Mr Muneer Ahmad **m** *Press Attaché*
Mr Shafiq Ahmad Shahzad **m** *Counsellor (Trade & Investment)*
Mr Chaudhry Nauman Zafar **m** *Counsellor / Director (Audit & Accounts)*
Mr Rehmat Ullah Khan **m** *Second Secretary (ACMA)*
Mr Ijaz Meherban **m** *Third Secretary (Audit & Accounts)*
Mr Aurang Zeb **m** *Deputy Assistant Director (MRP)*
Mr Rizwan Hussain **m** *Manager (NADRA)*

PALAU

London Honorary Consulate (see Honorary Consuls section below)

PANAMA

Embassy of Panama

40 Hertford Street W1J 7SH
020 7493 4646
Fax 020 7493 4333
panama1@btconnect.com

Consulate General
40 Hertford Street W1J 7SH
020 7409 2255
Fax 020 7493 4499
legalizations@panamaconsul.co.uk

HER EXCELLENCY MRS IRMA NATALIA ROYO RUIZ DE HAGERMAN **m** *Ambassador Extraordinary &*
Plenipotentiary (since 6 November 2019)
      Mr Santiago Hagerman Arnus
Miss Karla Patricia Gonzalez Rodriguez *Minister-Counsellor, Deputy Head of Mission*
Mr Luis Eduardo Pabon Chevalier **m** *Counsellor*
Mr Francisco J. Robayna *Political Attaché & Vice Consul*
Mrs Yanssy Aymee Gallardo Costillo * *Attaché*
Miss Daniela Lucia Pascale *Attaché (Cultural)*
Miss Anays Lisbeth Berrocal Corro *Representative to IMO*
Mr Luis Bernal Gonzalez **m** *Representative to IMO*
Mr Felix Oscar Sarlat Castillo **m** Alt. Representative II to IMO

PAPUA NEW GUINEA

Papua New Guinea High Commission
14 Waterloo Place SW1Y 4AR
020 7930 0922
Fax 020 7930 0828
kunduldn3@btconnect.com
www.pnghighcomm.org.uk
Monday-Friday 09.00-17.00

HER EXCELLENCY MS WINNIE ANNA KIAP *High Commissioner (since 24 August 2011)*
Ms Judith Silau *1st Secretary*

PARAGUAY

Embassy of the Republic of Paraguay
Ground and Lower Ground Floors, 81-83 Cromwell Road, London, SW7 5BW
Phone: 020 7610 4180
Fax: 020 7371 4297
Email: embaparuk@paraguayembassy.co.uk
Web: www.paraguayembassy.co.uk
Hours: Monday-Friday 09.30 to 17.00

Consular Section
Phone: 020 7610 4180
Hours: Monday-Friday 10.00 to 16.00

HIS EXCELLENCY MR GENARO VICENTE PAPPALARDO AYALA **m**
Ambassador Extraordinary & Plenipotentiary (since 31 March 2017)
      Mrs Romina Araujo de Pappalardo

Mrs Mirtha Beatriz Gonzalez Bogado *Minister*
Mr Blas Alfredo Felip Himmelreich **m** *Counsellor*
Captain Oscar Luis Noguera Ferreira **m** *Defence Attaché*

PERU

Embassy of Peru
52 Sloane Street SW1X 9SP
020 7235 7213/8340/3802

postmaster@peruembassy-uk.com
www.peruembassy-uk.com
Monday-Friday 09.00-17.00

Defence Attaché's Office
5 Fallstaff House, 24 Bardolph Road, Richmond TW9 2LH
020 8940 7773
Fax 020 8940 7735
agredef.granbretana@marine.pe

Trade Office
25a Motcomb Street,
London SW1X 8JU
020 7078 8287
info@promperu.uk

Consulate General
52 Sloane Street SW1X 9SP
020 7838 9223/9224
Fax 020 7823 2789
consulperu-londres@rree.gob.pe
Monday-Friday 09.30-13.00

HIS EXCELLENCY MR JUAN CARLOS GAMARRA m *Ambassador Extraordinary & Plenipotentiary & Permanent Representative to the IMO* (since 1 October 2018)
        Mrs Désirée von Preussen de Gamarra
Mr Julio César Sánchez Cornejo m *Minister-Counsellor, Deputy Head of Mission & Alternate Permanent Representative to the IMO*
Mrs. Roxana Castro Aranda de Bollig * *Minister (Consul General)*
Rear Admiral Daniel Felipe Valencia Jauregui * *Defence Attaché & Alternate Permanent Representative to the IMO*
Colonel Alfredo Miguel Ramón Pérez Urteaga m *Deputy Defence & Military Attaché*
Colonel Mario Lucar Delgado m *Police Attaché*
Mr José Augusto Pacheco de Freitas m *Counsellor (Political Affairs)*
 Mr Ricardo Leonardo Enrique Malca Alvariño *Counsellor (Press and Cultural Affairs) & Alternate Permanent Representative to the IMO*
Mr Ricardo Eli Romero Talledo *Counsellor for Economic & Commercial Affairs*
Captain Oscar Arturo Garrido-Lecca Hoyle m *Deputy Defence Attaché & Alternate Permanent Representative to the IMO*
Captain Gustavo Enrique Livia Rosas m *Alternate Permanent Representative to the IMO*
Major Elizabeth Gina Peralta Espinoza * *Deputy Police Attaché*
Miss Cosette Israel Campos Nieto *Second Secretary (Economic & Investment Affairs)*
Mr Dael Carlos Davila Elguera m *Third Secretary (Deputy Consul)*

PHILIPPINES

Embassy of the Republic of the Philippines
6-11 Suffolk Street SW1Y 4HG
020 7451 1780
Fax: 020 7930 9787
embassy@philemb.co.uk
london.pe@dfa.gov.ph
http://londonpe.dfa.gov.ph
Monday-Friday 09.00-17.00

Consular Section: 020 7451 1803/1814/1815/1819
Political (Bilateral) Section: 020 7451 1806
Political (Multilateral) Section: 020 7451 1808
Cultural Section: 020 7451 1804
Economic Section: 020 7451 1812
Administration Section: 020 7451 1812

Labour & Welfare Section

3rd Floor, 6 Suffolk Street SW1Y 4HG
020 7839 8078/020 7451 1832
Fax 020 7839 7345
polo_london@dole.gov.ph

Defence & Armed Forces Section (Non-Resident)
Calle Guadalquivir, 6 28002 Madrid
0034 915 644 833/0034 917 823 830 (loc 817)
Fax 0034 915 644 833
phildafa90spain@yahoo.com

Trade Section
1a Cumberland House Kensington Court W8 5NX
020 7937 1898/7998
Fax 020 7937 2747
london@dti.gov.ph
london@philippinetrade.org
www.investphilippines.gov.ph

Tourism Section
2nd Floor, 10-11 Suffolk Street SW1Y 4HG
020 7321 0668
Fax 020 7925 2920
info@itsmorefuninthephilippines.co.uk

Maritime Section
3rd Floor, 10 Suffolk Street SW1Y 4HG
020 7839 1650
aflingad@marina.gov.ph

HIS EXCELLENCY MR ANTONIO MANUEL LAGDAMEO m *Ambassador Extraordinary and Plenipotentiary &*
Permanent Representative to the IMO (since 20 February 2017)
               Mrs Maria Linda Lagdameo
Ms Arlene Gonzales-Macaisa * *Minister & Consul General*
Ms Rhenita Rodriguez *Minister & Consul General*
Ms Ana Marie Hernando *Minister & Consul & Alternate Permanent Representative to the IMO*
Mr Niño Anthony Balagtas m *2nd Secretary*
Ms Stacy Danika Alcantara-Garcia m *3rd Secretary & Vice Consul (Consular)*
Ms Beatriz Alexandra Martinez *3rd Secretary & Vice Consul (Administrative & Economic)*
Mr Medardo Albano m *Attaché (Finance)*
Ms Maria Theresa Jesusa Albano m *Attaché (Administration)*
Ms Aleth Panopio m *Attaché (Consular)*
Ms Jehli Liggayu * *Attaché (Administration)*
Ms Rosalyn del Valle Fajardo m *Attaché (Finance)*
Ms Mauro Fajardo III m *Attaché (Consular)*
Ms Eleanor Regalado m *Attaché (Consular)*
Mr Ronald Allan Fernandez *Attaché (Communications)*
Mr Michael John Angeles m *Attaché (Protocol)*
Ms Raida Acraman m *Attaché (Consular)*
Ms Grace Bañez m *Attaché (Political)*
Mrs Maria Liza Manarin m *Attaché (Administration)*
Ms Michelle Fatima Sanchez *Commercial Counsellor*
Ms Amuerfina Reyes * *Labour Attaché*
Mr Gerard Panga m *Tourism Attaché*
Capt Weniel Azcuna m *Technical Adviser to Maritime Attaché*
Ms Sheila Mae Aguilar *Welfare Officer*

POLAND

Embassy of the Republic of Poland
47 Portland Place W1B 1JH
020 7291 3520
Fax 020 7291 3576
london@msz.gov.pl
www.london.mfa.gov.pl

Economic Section
Bravura House 10 Bouverie Street EC4Y 8AX
020 7822 8917
london.we@msz.gov.pl

Polish Cultural Institute
Bravura House 10 Bouverie Street EC4Y 8AX
020 7822 8990
Fax 020 7822 8951
pci@polishculture.org.uk
www.polishculture.org.uk

Consular Section
Bravura House 10 Bouverie Street EC4Y 8AX
020 7822 8900/1
Fax 020 7936 3571
londyn.konsulat@msz.gov.pl
www.london.mfa.gov.pl

HIS EXCELLENCY PROFESSOR ARKADY JÓZEF RZEGOCKI m *Ambassador Extraordinary & Plenipotentiary (since 30 August 2016)*
             Mrs Jolanta Rzegocka
Mrs Agnieszka Kowalska m *Deputy Head of Mission, First Counsellor*
Mr Mateusz Stąsiek m *Consul General, First Counsellor*
Mr Michal Stanislaw Swierzowski m *First Counsellor*
Colonel Mieczyslaw Malec * *Defence Attaché*
Mr Robert Pawlicki m *Deputy Defence Military, Naval & Air Attaché*
Colonel Tomasz Ferfecki * *Deputy Defence Attaché*
Mrs Marta de Zuniga m *Minster-Counsellor (Deputy Director of the Polish Cultural Institute)*
Mr Tomasz Mariusz Wielgomas *Minister Counsellor*
Mr Mateusz Jozef Stasiek m *1st Counsellor/Consul General*
Ms Malgorzata Anna Buszynska *1st Counsellor/Permanent Representative to the IMO*
Mr Radoslaw Tadeusz Pytlak m *1st Counsellor (Head of Security)*
Mr Andrzej Kazimierz Krężel m *Counsellor (Head of Economic Section)*
Mr Krzysztof Andrzej Markiewicz *Counsellor*
Ms Sylwia Jolanta Cugier *Counsellor (Political)*
Mr Dariusz Wencel *Counsellor*
Mrs Katarzyna Szaran m *3rd Secretary (Head of Media and Public Diplomacy)*
Mr Konrad Zielinski m *2nd Secretary (Deputy Director of the Polish Cultural Institute)*
Lt Col Bartosz Wojciech Furgała m *Counsellor (Liaison Officer of Polish Police)*
Mrs Izabella Irmina Gołaszewska-Mazek m *3rd Secretary (Head of Estates)*
Mr Sylwester Lis m *Counsellor*
Mrs Maja Żywioł m *Counsellor*
Ms Monika Anna Dobkowska *1st Secretary (Political)*
Ms Joanna Urszula Górzyńska m *1st Secretary (Consular Affairs)*
Mrs Katarzyna Maria Hopkin m *1st Secretary (Consular Affairs)*
Miss Karolina Karina Orzechowska *1st Secretary (Protocol)*
Mr Radoslaw Gromski m *2nd Secretary*
Mrs Maria Niesluchowska m *2nd Secretary (Consular Affairs*
Mr Tomasz Edward Polkowski m *2nd Secretary (IT Department)*
Mr Tomasz Wieslaw Balcerowski m *2nd Secretary/Vice-Consul*
Mr Krzysztof Adam Zieliński m *2nd Secretary (Political)*
Mr Lukasz Karol Smalec m *2nd Secretary (Economic Section)*
Mr Chrzanowski Zbigniew *2nd Secretary (IT Specialist)*
Mr Bogusz Rafal Niesluchowski m *2nd Secretary*
Ms Dorota Maria Śpiewak *3rd Secretary (Vice Consul)*
Mrs Izabela Smalec m *3rd* Secretary *(Vice Consul)*
Ms Martyna Lesica *3rd Secretary (Consular Affairs)*
Mr Szymon Mieszko Szaran m *3rd Secretary (Political)*

Mrs Katarzyna Szaran **m** *3rd Secretary* *(Head of Media and Public Diplomacy)*
Ms Paulina Izabela Stepień **m** *Head of Finance*
Mrs Beata Jadwiga Sudar **m** *3rd Secretary*
Mr Arkadiusz Marek Cygan **m** *3rd Secretary (Economic)*
Mr Krzysztof Stolarczyk * *Warrant Officer*
Ms Jowita Wencius *Vice Consul*
Mr Michal Lukasz Zawiasa *Consular Attaché*
Ms Patrycja Wozniak *Consular Attaché*

PORTUGAL

Embassy of Portugal
11 Belgrave Square SW1X 8PP
020 7235 5331
Fax 020 7235 0739
londres@mne.pt

Trade & Tourism
020 7201 6666
Fax 020 7201 6633
trade.london@portugalglobal.pt
tourism.london@portugalglobal.pt

Consulate General
3 Portland Place W1B 1HR
020 7291 3770
Fax 020 7291 3799
consulado.londres@mne.pt

HIS EXCELLENCY MR MANUEL LOBO ANTUNES **m** *Ambassador Extraordinary & Plenipotentiary (since 2 September 2016)*
　　　Mrs Maria Plantier Santos Lobo Antunes
Mr Antonio Jose Marques Sabido Costa **m** *Minister-Counsellor,*
Mrs Cristina Maria Cerqueira Pucarinho **m** *Consul General*
Mr José Rui Constantino da Silva **m** *Deputy Consul General*
Mr João Nuno Sousa de Albuquerque *1st Secretary*
Mr Pedro de Moraes Sarmento Patrício *Counsellor (Economic & Commercial)*
Ms Helena Paula de Sousa e Silva Fernandes *Press Attaché*
Mr Nuno Ernesto Dias Sebastiao *Chancellor*
Ms Cláudia Cristina Marques Miguel *Attaché (Tourism)*
Dr Regina Duarte *Attaché (Educational Affairs)*
Mrs Maria Joao Leal da Silva Freire Morgado *Attaché (Legal Affairs)*
Ms Ana Paula Prazeres de Almeida *Attaché (Tourism PR and Press)*
Mr Renato Filipe Aires Alves Dores Tiago *Consular Attaché*

QATAR

Embassy of the State of Qatar
1 South Audley Street, London W1K 1NB
020 7493 2200
Fax 020 7493 2661
Monday-Friday 09.30-16.00
amblondon@mofa.gov.qa
amb@qatarembassy.org.uk

Cultural Section
47 Park Lane W1K 1PR
020 8076 1111
Fax 0208 076 1413
secretary-uk@edu.gov.qa

Medical Section
30 Collingham Gardens, London, SW5 0HN

020 7370 6871
Fax 020 7835 1469
qatmeduk@qatarhealth.co.uk

Military Section
21 Hertford Street London W1J 7RY
020 7409 2229
Fax 020 7629 0740
mfahmi@qda.qa

His Excellency Fahad Bin Mohammed Al-Attiyah **m** *Ambassador Extraordinary & Plenipotentiary (since 27 January 2022)*
        Shaikha Raya Khalifa Abdullah Al-Khalifa

Mr Hamad Bin Khalifa Bin Hamad Al-Thani **m** *Minister-Counsellor*
Mr Hamad Bin Jassim J M Al-Thani **m** *Minister-Counsellor*
Mr Mohamed Abdulla Al-Jabir m *Minister Plenipotentiary (Deputy Head of Mission)*
Colonel Ali Mohamed A Al-Fadala **m** *Defence Attaché*
Mr Jassim Moftah J. M. Al-Moftah **m** *First Secretary*
Sheikh Abdulla Jassim Al-Thani m *First Secretary*
Mr Mohammed Abdulaziz M A Al-Attiyah *First Secretary*
Mr Ghanim Abdulrahman Al-Hodaifi Al-Kuwari **m** *First Secretary*
Sheikh Salman Jassim Al-Thani **m** *Second Secretary*
Ms Maha Yousuf Al-Baker *Second Secretary*
Mr Abdulrahman Mohamed Al-Baker * *Second Secretary-Consul*
Ms Reem Yousuf A.S. Alharami *Second Secretary*
Mr Fahad Abdulla S M Al-Mana *Communications Attaché*
Mr Abdulla Al-Ghanim *Commercial Attaché*
Mr Abdulla Ali Al-Ansari **m** *Medical Attaché*
Capt Khalid Nasser Al-Sulaiti *Assistant Defence Attaché*
Mr Abdulla Mohammed A H Al-Attiyah *Assistant Academic Military Attaché*
Staff Col Jaralla Hamad M.A. Al-Nabit m *Second Assistant Defence Attaché*
Mr Mohammed Rashid Al - Kuwari * *First Secretary/ Military Students Affairs*
Ms Ameena Salman Al-Meer *1st Secretary (Senior Academic Adviser)*
Mr Fahad Al-Kuwari **m** *Cultural Attaché*
Mr Ibrahim Al-Fadala **m** *Student Supervisor*

ROMANIA

Embassy of Romania
Arundel House, 4 Palace Green, London, W8 4QD
Phone: 020 7937 9666
Fax: 020 7937 8069
Email: londra@mae.ro
Web: www.londra.mae.ro
Hours: Monday-Friday 09.00 to 17.00

Defence Attaché's Office
Arundel House, 4 Palace Green, London, W8 4QD
Phone: 020 7937 4379
Fax: 020 7937 4379
Email: londra.aparare@mae.ro

Home Affairs Attaché's Office
Arundel House, 4 Palace Green, London, W8 4QD
Phone: 020 7937 9666
Fax: 020 7937 8069
Email: londra.mai@mae.ro

Commercial Section
Arundel House, 4 Palace Green, London, W8 4QD
Phone: 020 7937 9668
Fax: 020 7937 8069

Email: londra.economic@mae.ro

Labour and Social Affairs Attaché's Office
Arundel House, 4 Palace Green, London, W8 4QD
Email: londra.social@mae.ro

Romanian Cultural Institute
1 Belgrave Square, London, SW1X 8PH
Phone: 020 7752 0134
Email: office@icr-london.co.uk
Email: www.icr-london.co.uk

HER EXCELLENCY MRS DANIELA LAURA POPESCU m
Ambassador Extraordinary & Plenipotentiary (since 5 March 2021)
      Mr Antonie Popescu
Mr Alexandru Dodan m *Deputy Head of Mission, Minister Plenipotentiary*
Colonel Iulian Adrian Costea m *Defence Military Air and Naval Attaché*
Mr Daniel Robert Adrian Marin m *Minister Plenipotentiary (Political and Consular)*
Ms Mary-Eliana Teodorescu *Minister Plenipotentiary (Political)*
Mr Gabriel-Alexandru Marica m *Minister Plenipotentiary*
Mrs Gilda Luiza Truică m *Minister Counsellor (Political)*
Ms Maria Artene *Minister-Counsellor (Political)*
Mr Mihai Cristian Ioan *Minister Counsellor (Political)*
Mr Mihail Bogdan Mihăilescu *Minister Counsellor (Economic & Trade)*
Mrs Laura Tiu m *Minister-Counsellor (Consular)*
Mrs Laura Nicoleta Nasta m *Minister Counsellor (Economic Affairs)*
Mr Aurel Mailat *Counsellor (Political)*
Major Ovidiu Ştefan Poiană m *Deputy Defence Military Air and Naval Attaché*
Mr Gheorghiţă-Florin Ciornei m *2nd Secretary (Political)*
Ms Georgiana-Corina Giunca *2nd Secretary (Political)*
Mr Vlad Vida m *Counsellor (Home Affairs Attaché)*
Mrs Mihaela Nica m *Attaché (Labour & Social Affairs)*
Ms Ileana Stănică m *Attaché (Labour & Social Affairs)*
Mrs Camelia Oprescu *Consul General*
Mrs Cătălina Marica m *Consul General*
Mr Mihai Tiu m *Consul*
Mr Marius Voinescu m *Vice Consul*
Mr Tiberiu Raicu m *Attaché (Communications)*

RUSSIA

Embassy of the Russian Federation (Main Building)
6/7 Kensington Palace Gardens, London, W8 4QP
Phone: 020 7229 6412
Fax: 020 7727 8625
Email: kanc@rusemb.org.uk
Web: www.rusemb.org.uk

Embassy of the Russian Federation (Residence of the Ambassador)
13 Kensington Palace Gardens, London, W8 4QX
Phone: 020 7229 3620 / 020 7229 7281
Fax: 020 7229 5804

Consular Department
5 Kensington Palace Gardens, London, W8 4QS
Phone: 020 3668 7474
Email: info@rusemb.org.uk
Web: www.rusemb.org.uk/consulate

Defence Attaché's Office
44 Millfield Lane, London, N6 6JB
Phone: 020 8341 7979
Fax: 020 8341 7744

Office of the Trade Representative
33 Highgate West Hill, London, N6 6NL
Phone: 020 8340 1907
Fax: 020 8348 0112
Web: www.rustrade.org.uk

HIS EXCELLENCY MR ANDREI KELIN m
Ambassador Extraordinary & Plenipotentiary (since 21 November 2019)
Mrs Irina Kelina

Mr Ivan Volodin m *Minister-Counsellor*
Mr Boris Abramov m *Trade Representative*
Mr Maxim Elovik m *Military Attaché*
Mr Denis Piminov m *Senior Counsellor*
Mrs Olga Zykova m *Counsellor*
Mr Kirill Sokolov-Shsherbachev m *Counsellor (Head of Consular Section)*
Mr Gennady Antonov m *Counsellor*
Mr Stanislav Antipin *Counsellor*
Mr Aleksandr Khlopianov m *Counsellor*
Mr Boris Zhelezov *Counsellor*
Mr Ilya Erofeev m *Counsellor*
Mrs Ksenia Verkholantseva m *Counsellor*
Mr Arsen Daduani m *1st Secretary*
Mr Yury Boychenko m *1st Secretary*
Mr Konstantin Timokhin m *1st Secretary (Alternate Permanent Representative to the IMO)*
Mr Evgeny Skobkarev m *1st Secretary*
Mr Konstantin Yushmanov m *2nd Secretary*
Mr Ilya Tolstykh m *2nd Secretary*
Mr Stepan Anikeev m *2nd Secretary*
Miss Mariam Semenova *2nd Secretary*
Miss Nina Mishchenko *2nd Secretary (Head of the Ambassador's Office)*
Mr Timofey Kunitskiy m *2nd Secretary*
Mr Igor Pavlov *2nd Secretary*
Mr Ivan Gozhev m *2nd Secretary*
Mr Kirill Gruzdev m *3rd Secretary*
Mr Andrey Bugaets m *3rd Secretary*
Mr Aleksandr Iarovoi *3rd Secretary*
Mr Dmitry Golubovskiy m *3rd Secretary*
Mrs Anastasia Erofeeva m *3rd Secretary*
Mr Viacheslav Polevoi m *Attaché*
Mr Dmitry Ananiev m *Attaché*
Mr Aleksandr Soin m *Attaché*
Ms Elena Marchan *Attaché*
Ms Natalia Zatulko *Attaché*
Mr Alexander Trubachev m *Attaché*
Mr Evgeny Kiselev m *Attaché*
Mr Sergey Konev * *Attaché*
Mr Nikolai Romanov *Attaché*
Ms Ekaterina Tatarnikova *Attaché*

RWANDA

Rwanda High Commission
120-122 Seymour Place, London, W1H 1NR
Phone: 020 7224 9832
Fax: 020 7724 8642
Email: uk@rwandainuk.gov.rw
Web: www.rwandainuk.gov.rw

Vacant *High Commissioner*
Mr James Wizeye m *Minister Counsellor, Chargé d'Affaires*
Mr Joseph Kabakeza m *1st Counsellor*
Mr Johnson Rwigema *1st Secretary*

SAINT CHRISTOPHER & NEVIS

High Commission for Saint Christopher & Nevis
10 Kensington Court W8 5DL
020 7937 9718
Fax 020 937 7484
mission@sknhc.co.uk
www.stkittsnevishcuk.gov.kn

HIS EXCELLENCY DR KEVIN M. ISAAC **m** *High Commissioner (since 12 January 2011)*
        Mrs Prangtip Isaac
Mrs Elsa G. Wilkin-Armbrister **m** *Minister-Counsellor (Investment and Further Development)*
Mr Gurdip Bath **m** *Commercial Attaché (Business & Trade)*

SAINT LUCIA

High Commission for Saint Lucia
1 Collingham Gardens SW5 0HW
020 7370 7123
Fax 020 7370 1905
enquiries@stluciahcuk.org

MR GUY MAYERS **m** *High Commissioner (since 17 December 2016)*
        Mrs Hannah Ruth Mayers
Mrs Leonne Theodore-John * *Minister-Counsellor*
Mr Enrico Louis Monfrini Counsellor (Economic)
Mrs Rose-Anne Evelyn-Bates **m** *1st Secretary (Political)*
Mrs Veronica Francis-Joseph * *Vice Consul*

SAINT VINCENT & THE GRENADINES

High Commission for Saint Vincent & the Grenadines
10 Kensington Court, London, W8 5DL
Phone: 020 7460 1256 / 020 7565 2874
Email: info@svghighcom.co.uk
Web: www.svghighcom.co.uk / www.gov.vc

High Commissioner's Office
Phone: 020 7565 2874
Email: office@svghighcom.co.uk

Political & Commercial Section
Phone: 020 7565 2885
Email: mc@svghighcom.co.uk

Consular Section
Phone: 020 7460 2588
Email: info@svghighcom.co.uk

HIS EXCELLENCY MR CENIO E. LEWIS **m**
High Commissioner (since 24 April 2001)
        Mrs Ita Lewis

Miss Jinelle Kinique Adams *Minister Counsellor*
Mrs Carolin de Freitas-Sawh **m** *Counsellor*

SAMOA

High Commission of the Independent State of Samoa
Avenue Commandant Lothaire 1, 1040 Brussels
+32 2 660 8454
Fax +32 2 675 0336
samoaembassy@skynet.be

London Honorary Consulate (see Honorary Consuls section below)

Vacant *High Commissioner*
Ms Fiona Lene-Samoa **m** *Counsellor & Deputy Head of Mission*
Ms Maxine Hunter *First Secretary*

SAN MARINO

Embassy of the Republic of San Marino
All correspondence should be addressed to the Department of Foreign Affairs
Palazzo Begni – Contrada Omerelli 47890 San Marino – Republic of San Marino
+378 (0549) 883602
Fax +378 (0549) 882422
amb.regounitio@gov.sm

London Honorary Consulate (see Honorary Consuls section below)

HER EXCELLENCY DR SILVIA MARCHETTI *Ambassador Extraordinary & Plenipotentiary* (since 25 September 2018)

SÃO TOMÉ & PRINCIPE

Embassy of São Tomé & Principe
175 Avenue de Tervuren 1150 Brussels
00322 734 8966
Fax 00322 734 8815
Ambassade@saotomeeprincipe.be

London Honorary Consulate (see Honorary Consuls section below)

Vacant *Ambassador Extraordinary & Plenipotentiary*
Mr Armindo de Brito **m** *Chargé d'Affaires a.i.*
Mr Horatio Fernando da Forseca **m** *2nd Secretary*

SAUDI ARABIA

Royal Embassy of Saudi Arabia
30 Charles Street, Mayfair W1J 5DZ.
020 7917 3000

Defence Attaché's Office
26 Queens Gate, SW7 5JE
020 7581 7070

Diplomatic Office of the Cultural Bureau
630 Chiswick High Road, London W4 5RY
020 3249 7000

Medical Section
Building 3, Cheswick Park
Cheswick High Road, W4 5YA
020 8863 2200

Consular Office
32 Charles Street, Mayfair W1J 5DZ
020 7917 3000

Economic Section
30 Charles Street, Mayfair W1J 5DZ
020 7917 3000

Commercial Section

15/16 Queens Street, Mayfair W1J 5PQ
020 7723 7817

Islamic Affairs Section
2nd Floor Park Lorne, 111 Park Road NW8 7JL
020 7723 7817

Information Section
30 Charles Street, Mayfair W1J 5DZ
020 7917 3000

HIS EXCELLENCY HRH Prince Khalid Bin Bandar Bin Sultan Al-Saud m *Ambassador Extraordinary &*
Plenipotentiary (since 01 July 2019)
      HH Princess Lucy Caroline Al-Saud
Mr Hassan Saeed I Al Jomae m *Counsellor – Deputy Head of Mission*
H H Prince Sultan Fahad Abdullah Al-Saud m *Minister Plenipotentiary*
Mr Saud N H Al Hamdan m *Minister Plenipotentiary*
Mr Ahmed Saleh A Al Shehri m *Counsellor (Head of Administration & Communication Department)*
Mr Lafi Falah L Al Mutairi m *Counsellor (International Organisations Department)*
Mr Sulaiman Mohammed S Al Anbar *Counsellor*
Mr Khalid Omar m Basfar m *1st Secretary*
Miss Hend Ibrahim S Al Ibrahim *1st Secretary*
Mr Hassan Mohamed Al Ahmari m *1st Secretary*
Mr Ammar Fahad I Al Ammar m *1st Secretary*
Ms Sarah Ismail I Al Shoura *1st Secretary*
Mr Ahmed Abdullah Al Hamaidi m *1st Secretary*
Mr Talal Tolahian S Al Harbi m *1st Secretary*
Mr Fahad Mansour KH Ben Garmalah m *2nd Secretary*
Mr Khalid Hamed M Bakhsh *2nd Secretary*
Ms Jamila Haif M Al-Khatani m *2nd Secretary*
Mr Nasser Mohammed A Al-Thuwainy * *3rd Secretary*
H.H Prince Sultan Bin Jalawi A. Bin Mousaad Al Saud *3rd Secretary*
Mr Saud Abdulaziz A Al-Fadhli *3rd Secretary*
Mr Shakir Hassan A Al Sharif *3rd Secretary*
Mr Abdullah Mohammed S Al Qarni m *3rd Secretary*
Mr Mohammed Shajaan A. Al Ogaili * *3rd Secretary*
Mr Waleed Suleiman KH Al-Natheer m *3rd Secretary*
Mr Hatem Abo Gamel m *3rd Secretary*
Mr Fawaz Ali S Al Maiman m *3rd Secretary*
Mr Sultan Rashed M. Al Shehri *3rd Secretary*
Mr Mouath Saeed Al Ghamdi *3rd Secretary*
Mr Abdulrahman Mohammed Al Fwzan m *3rd Secretary*
Mr Abdulrahman Jamal A Al Jama m *3rd Secretary*
Mr Abdullah Yousel Al Khalaf m *3rd Secretary*
Mr Naif Hussain M Tami m *3rd Secretary*
Mr Faisal Abdulaziz H Al Saleh m *3rd Secretary*
Mr Abdulaziz Aladham A Al Onazi m *Attaché*
Miss Njoud Zaid T Al Khudairy *Attaché*
Mr Nawaf Faiez Y Al Thari *Attaché*
Mr Bader H.A. Al-Harpi m *Attaché*
Mr Thunayyan Bin Thunayyan *Attaché*
Mr Yousef Ali M Al Oufi m *Attaché*
Mr Mushabbab Salem M Bin Hamran m *Attaché*
Mr Ali Zhuhar H Al Shehri m *Attaché*
Mr Fahad Abdulrahman A. Al Muhaya *Attaché*
Mr Mushref Abdullah S. Al Amri m *Attaché*
Mr Thamer Mohammed A. Al Akeel m *Attaché*
Mr Mohammed Mansour H Al Mahyoubi *Attaché*
Mr Asker Mohammed A Benasaker m *Attaché (Head of Information Office)*
Mr Mohammed Masoud S Al Ghamdi *Attaché (Information Office)*
Mr Waleed Awad A A Al Awad m *Attaché (Communications Department)*
HRH Prince Abdulaziz Bin Mishal Bin Badr Bin Saud Abdulaziz Al Saud m *Attaché*
Mr Saeed Hallas S Al Orfan m *Attaché*
Mr Arif Awadh J Al Harbi m *Attaché*
Brig General Riyadh Mohammed A. Aboabat m *Defence Attaché*

Col Pilot Mohammed Saeed A Al Shahrani m *Assistant Military Attaché*
Lt Col Bandaer Hamid S Ahmed m *Assistant Attaché*
Col Mubark Mesfer A Al Qahtani m *Assistant Attaché*
Col Faisal Abdulmajeed Al Khayyal * *Assistant Military Attaché*
Major Ahmed Nasser A Asiri m *Deputy Land Forces Attaché*
Col Pilot Badr Abdulrahman F Al Mubarak m *Training Manager (Airforce Affairs)*
Mr Zegam Mohammad DH Al Tewalah m *Attaché (Defence)*
Col Khaled Saleh A Al Turki m *Attaché (Defence)*
Col Badr Eyadah A. Al-Eyadah m *Attaché (Defence)*
Lt Col Ahmed Abu Hadi m *Administrative Attaché*
Lt Col Abdulaziz Ibrahim M Al Bader m *Attaché*
Commander Abdullah Ayedh Al Harbi m *Attaché (Defence)*
Lt Commander Zakariya Abdullah M Al-Said m *Attaché (Defence)*
Mr Loai Abdulaziz F Al Fraih m *Attaché (Defence)*
Major Ahmad Ali A Al Assiri m *Attaché (Defence)*
Major Ibrahim Hamad I Bin Masoud * *Attaché (Defence)*
HRH Prince Abdulaziz Bin Saif Alnasr Bin Saud Bin Abdulaziz Al Saud m *Attaché (Defence)*
Lieutenant Muhannad Moneer M Al-Fakhrani m *Attaché (Defence)*
Eng Moataz Ibrahim A Al-Aqel m *Attaché (Defence)*
Mr Omar Hammad O. Al-Ghofaili m *Attaché (Head of Accounts Department)*
Mr Abdulaziz Hamad S Al Suwilem m *Attaché (Defence)*
Mr Saud Khalf M Al Anazi m *Attaché (Defence)*
Dr Amal Jamel Y. Fatani m *Cultural Attaché*
Dr Adel Abdulrahman Al-Yobi m *Attaché (Cultural)*
Dr Abdulaziz Saleh Al-Raddadi m *Attaché (Cultural Office Academic Advisor)*
Dr Talal Ghazi N Al-Harbi m *Attaché (Cultural Office Academic Advisor)*
Dr Faisal Mohammad A Al Shareef m *Attaché (Cultural)*
Dr Madallah AlRokwi M Al Enazi m *Attaché (Cultural)*
Mr Abdullah Ibrahim M Al Othman m *Attaché (Cultural)*
Mr Abdullah Abdulrahman A Bin Saeedan m *Attaché (Cultural)*
Mr Khalid Abdulrahman Al Yousef m *Attaché (Cultural)*
Mr Abdullah Hamad M Al Anazi m *Attaché (Cultural)*
Mr Bader Saeed O Al Omar m *Attaché (Cultural)*
Mr Osama Mansour G Al Jehani *Attaché (Information Office)*
Mr Majed Hadi Al Kahtani m *Attaché (Information Office)*
Mr Hamdan Nawar A Al Otaibi m *Attaché (Commercial Office)*
Mr Abdulaziz Hamoud A Al Ghifaili m *Attaché (SAGIA's Office)*
Dr Adnan Ibrahim A Al Sarawi m *Health Attaché*
Dr Ibraheem Khalifa Al Hanout m *Assistant to the Health Attaché*
Dr Ahmed Al-Dubayan m *Attaché (Islamic Affairs)*
Dr Mohammed Ahmed F Al Faifi m *Attaché (Islamic Affairs)*
Mr Mansour Abdullah M Al-Aql m *Attaché*
Mr Ali F M Al-Omran m *Attaché*
Mr Saleh Abdullah S. Alshethri m *Attaché (Director of Internal Security)*
Mr Mohammad Abdulqader M Abu Aabid m *Attaché (Deputy Head of Embassy Security)*
Mr Abdulaziz Mohammed Y Al Nojaime m *Attaché*
Brig. Gen. Hussain S Al-Kahtani m *Assistant Defence Attaché (Air)*

SENEGAL

Embassy of the Republic of Senegal
39 Marloes Road, London, W8 6LA
Phone: 020 7938 4048 / 020 7937 7237
Fax: 020 7938 2546
Email: senegalembassy@hotmail.co.uk
Web: www.senegal-embassy.uk

HER EXCELLENCY DR FATIMATA DIA m
Ambassador Extraordinary & Plenipotentiary (since 29 November 2019)
        Mr Nouhamadou Falilou Diague
Mr Cheikh Tidiane Deme m *1st Counsellor*
Mr Dramane Samoura m *2nd Counsellor*
Mrs Collette Thiakane Faye m 2nd *Counsellor*
Mr Papa Cheikh Sylla m *1st Secretary*
Mr Ibrahima Sall m *1st Secretary*

Mrs Rokhaya Samb **m** *2nd Secretary*

SERBIA

Embassy of the Republic of Serbia
28 Belgrave Square, London, SW1X 8QB
Phone: 020 7235 9049
Fax: 020 7235 7092
Email: embassy.london@mfa.rs
Web: www.london.mfa.gov.rs

HER EXCELLENCY MRS ALEKSANDRA JOKSIMOVIĆ **m**
Ambassador Extraordinary & Plenipotentiary (since 1 December 2018)
        Mr Siniša Krajčinović
Mr Vladimir Dišović *Counsellor*
Mrs Neda Mijajlović * *Counsellor*
Miss Marijana Ognjanović *Counsellor (Consular Affairs)*
Mr Dejan Kostić * *2nd Secretary*
Mrs Stana Vučković **m** *Attaché*
Colonel Dragan Dabović **m** *Defence Attaché*
Lt Colonel Ilija Vujičić **m** *Assistant Defence Attaché*

SEYCHELLES

The High Commission of the Republic of Seychelles
130-132 Buckingham Palace Road SW1W 9SA
Tel: 020 7730 2046
office@seychelleshcl.co.uk
Monday-Friday 09.00-17.00

Consular Section
020 7730 2046
079 58433 877 (Emergency)

Commercial Section
020 7730 0700
seychelles@uksto.co.uk
www.seychelles.travel
Monday-Friday 09.00-17.00

Vacant *High Commissioner*
Mr Terry Romain *Acting High Commissioner, Principal Counsellor*

SIERRA LEONE

Sierra Leone High Commission
41 Eagle Street WC1R 4TL
020 7404 0140
Fax 020 7430 9862
info@slhc-uk.org.uk
www.slhc-uk.org.uk
Monday-Friday 09.30-13.00 & 14.00-17.00

HIS EXCELLENCY DR MORIE KOMBA MANYEH **m** *High Commissioner (since 15 October 2019)*
        Mrs Marie Manyeh
Mrs Yvonne Alexandrina King **m** *Deputy High Commissioner*
Mr Witson Tebeh Yankuba * *Minister-Counsellor/Head of Chancery*
Mr Christopher Bockarie **m** *Counsellor (Consular)*
Mr Joseph Lennox Maada Goakai * *Counsellor*
Mrs Agnes Simeonette Naomi During **m** *1st Secretary*
Mr Festus Kuyembeh * *Financial Attaché*
Mr Adulai Braima **m** *Information Attaché*

SINGAPORE

High Commission for the Republic of Singapore
9 Wilton Crescent, London, SW1X 8SP
Phone: 020 7235 8315
Fax: 020 7245 6583
Email: singhc_lon@mfa.sg
Web: http://mfa.gov.sg/london
Hours: Monday-Friday 09.00 to 17.00

Consular Section
Basement 9 Wilton Crescent, London, SW1X 8SP
Phone: 020 7235 8315
Fax: 020 7235 9850
Email: singhc_con_lon@mfa.sg
Hours: Monday-Friday 09.30 to 12.30

Liaison Office
Office No 214, 239 High Street Kensington, London, W8 6SN
Phone: 020 7960 6655 & 020 7960 6656

Commercial Section
Singapore Centre First Floor, Southwest House, 11A Regent Street, London, SW1Y 4LR
Phone: 020 7484 2730
Web: http://www.iesingapore.gov.sg

Maritime Section
Singapore Centre First Floor, Southwest House, 11A Regent Street, London, SW1Y 4LR
Phone: 020 7484 2738

HIS EXCELLENCY MR THUAN KUAN LIM **m**
High Commissioner (since 2 September 2020)
　　　　Mrs Gek Choo Patricia The
Ms Cheryl Lee Shui Lene * *Deputy High Commissioner & Counsellor*
Mr Kum Cheong Aw **m** *Counsellor (Security Liaison)*
Mr Wai Yoke Wong * *Counsellor (Liaison Office)*
Mr Vishnuvarthan *Balakrishnan* **m** *Counsellor (Admin & Consular)*
Ms Caitlin Chay Jialing **m** *2nd Secretary (Political)*
Ms Ang Hui Teng **m** *1st Secretary (Commercial)*
Mr Hanqiang Tan **m** *1st Secretary (Maritime)*
Mr Darrick Yong En Leow *1st Secretary (Maritime)*
Peh Min-Min, Valerie *1st Secretary*
Mr Lau Yu Chin Leon *2nd Secretary (Political)*
Ms Khairin Nazura Binte Khamaruldin *Attaché (Admin & Consular)*
Ms Celest Yin Hsien Chang **m** *Attaché (Admin & Technical)*

SLOVAKIA

Embassy of Slovakia
25 Kensington Palace Gardens, London, W8 4QY

The premises of the Embassy of Slovakia are currently under renovation
Temporary address: 17 Connaught Place, 5th Floor, London, W2 2ES

Phone: 020 7313 6480
Fax: 020 7313 6481
Email: emb.london@mzv.sk
Web: www.mzv.sk/londyn
Hours: Monday-Thursday 08.30 to 16.45
　　　　Friday 08.30 to 15.30

Consular & Visa Section

Temporary address: 18 Stanhope Place, Ground Floor, London, W2 2HB
Phone: 020 7313 6470
Email: cons.london@mzv.sk
Hours: Monday-Thursday 09.00 to 12.00 & 13.00 to 16.00
        Friday 09.00 to 12.00 & 13.00 to 15.00

Commercial Department
Phone: 020 7313 6484

Defence Attaché's Office
Phone/Fax: 020 7722 3650

HIS EXCELLENCY MR RÓBERT ONDREJCSÁK m
Ambassador Extraordinary & Plenipotentiary (since 27 December 2020)
        Mrs Maryna Vorotnyuk
Mr Marcel Babicz m *Counsellor, Deputy Head of Mission*
Mr Marek Murín *Counsellor, Head of Consular Section*
Mr Karol Šefčík m *Counsellor (Consular)*
Ms Elena Mallicková *Counsellor (Cultural)*
Mr Michal Horvat m *1st Secretary (Economic)*
Ms Beatrix Pavlačková *3rd Secretary (Political, Protocol)*
Ms Marcela Matúšková *3rd Secretary (Consular)*
Ms Miroslava Raková *Attaché (Administrative)*
Mr Juraj Krázel m *Attaché (Administrative)*
Colonel Vladimír Stolárik m *Defence Attaché*
Colonel Ladislav Csémi m *Police Attaché*

SLOVENIA

Embassy of the Republic of Slovenia
17 Dartmouth Street
London SW1H 9BL
Tel.: 020 7222 5700
sloembassy.london@gov.si
www.london.embassy.si

Consular Section
Tel.: 020 7227 9711
E-mail:consular.london@gov.si
Monday to Thursday 10:00 – 13:00

HER EXCELLENCY MS SIMONA LESKOVAR *Ambassador Extraordinary & Plenipotentiary (since 22 September 2020)*
Mrs Darja Golež m *Minister Plenipotentiary, Deputy Head of Mission*
Mrs Katja Biloslav m *Minister Plenipotentiary - Consul*
Mrs Jana Bajec Povse * *Minister Plenipotentiary (Economics)*
Ms Petra Trkov *2nd Secretary*
Ms Tatjana Ikić *Attaché Correspondent*

SOLOMON ISLANDS

High Commission for the Solomon Islands

HIS EXCELLENCY MR ELIAM TANGIRONGO m *High Commissioner (Since 19 September 2018)*
        Mrs Anna Tangirongo
Mrs Clera Waokea Rotu m *2nd Secretary (Political)*

SOMALIA

Embassy of the Federal Republic of Somalia

HIS EXCELLENCY MR ABDULKADIR AHMED KHEYR ABDI Ambassador Extraordinary & Plenipotentiary (since 25 November 2021)
Mr Dayib Mahamud Sheikh Ahmed 1st Counsellor, Deputy Head of Mission

SOUTH AFRICA
High Commission of the Republic of South Africa
South Africa House
Trafalgar Square WC2N 5DP
020 7451 7299
Fax 020 7839 5670
london.sahc@dirco.gov.za
London.info@dirco.gov.za

Home Affairs Section
15 Whitehall
SW1A 2DD
020 7925 89800/01
Fax 020 7839 5198
london.civic@dirco.gov.za
london.visa@dirco.gov.za

HER EXCELLENCY MS NOMATEMBA GUGULETHU PUDNIXIA OLIVIA TAMBO High Commissioner
Mrs Charmaine Estelle Fredericks m Deputy High Commissioner
Mr Ronald Sipho Jama Mbatha m Minister (Transport)
Brig-Gen Edward Ramabu m Defence Adviser
Ms Rasheeda Adam Counsellor (Political)
Ms Elizabeth Nkone Aphane Counsellor (Immigration & Civic Services)
Mr Marc Jürgens m Counsellor (Political)
Mrs Mogomotsi Vinolia Makwetla m Counsellor (ICT)
Lt Col Raisibe Letta Mmakola Counsellor (SAPS Liaison Officer)
Col Phineas Vusimuzi Mpela m Deputy Defence Adviser
Mr Tyrone Marc m First Secretary (Political)
Mr Pubudu Kenneth Mahlake m First Secretary (ICT)
Mrs Jenny Mcube m First Secretary (Corporate Services)
Mr Mpho Comfort Moloto First Secretary (ICT)
Ms Tshepiso Emmah Kube Second Secretary (Immigration and Civic Services)
Mr Ramoshoane Adam Sethosa m Second Secretary (Immigration and Civic Services)
Mr Sibusiso Ntando Maseko m Third Secretary (Corporate Services)
Ms Prudence Mabena Third Secretary (Corporate Services)
WO1 Nompumelelo Carol Radebe * Defence Office Chief Clerk

SOUTH SUDAN

Embassy of the Republic of South Sudan
22-25 Portman Close, W1H 6BS
020 36872366
info@embrss.org.uk
www.embrss.org.uk

HER EXCELLENCY MS AGNES ADLINO ORIFA OSWAHA Ambassador Extraordinary & Plenipotentiary (since 22 March 2021)
Mrs Ashwil Haruun Lual Ruun * Chargé d' Affaires a.i
Mr Maker Ayuel Deng m Minister Plenipotentiary
Brigadier General Charles Malet Kuol * Defence Attaché
Mr Majak Arop Kuol Arop m Counsellor
Mr George Isaac Kut Guj 3rd Secretary
Mr Giir Giir Majok Biar * Immigration Attaché
Mr Majong Kau Dut Immigration Officer

SPAIN

Embassy of Spain
39 Chesham Place SW1X 8SB

020 7235 5555
Fax 020 7259 5392
emb.londres@maec.es
www.exteriores.gob.es/Embajadas/londres/en
@EmbSpainUK

Consulate General
20 Draycott Place SW3 2RZ
020 7589 8989
0871 376 0023 (Visa Information)
Fax 020 7581 7888
cog.londres@maec.es
www.exteriores.gob.es/Consulados/londres/en

Cultural Office
39 Chesham Place SW1X 8SB
020 7201 5517/5522/5524
Fax 020 7259 6487
emb.londres.ofc@maec.es

Defence Office
1st Floor, 20 Peel Street W8 7PD
020 7313 9078
Fax 020 7792 4570
agredlon@oc.mde.es

Transport Office - Permanent Representation to the International Maritime Organization
39 Chesham Place SW1X 8SB
020 7201 5539
Fax 020 7235 9303
imo.spain@fomento.es

Education Office
20 Peel Street W8 7PD
020 7727 2462
Fax 020 7229 4965
info.uk@educacion.gob.es
www.educacion.gob.es/reinounido

Employment, Migrations & Social Security Office
20 Peel Street W8 7PD
020 7221 0098 / 020 7243 9897
Fax 020 7229 7270
reinounido@mitramiss.es
www.empleo.gob.es

Economic & Commercial Office
125 Old Broad Street EC2N 1AR
020 7776 7730
Fax 020 7374 8896
londres@comercio.mineco.es

Agriculture, Fisheries & Food Office
39 Chesham Place SW1X 8SB
020 7235 5005
Fax 020 7259 6897
londres@mapa.es

Press & Communications Office
39 Chesham Place SW1X 8SB
020 7235 7537
Fax 020 7235 2263
londres@comunicacion.presidencia.gob.es

Liaison Magistrate Unit
39 Chesham Place SW1X 8SB

020 7235 5555
Fax 020 7259 5392
enlace.reinounido@justicia.es

HIS EXCELLENCY MR JOSÉ PASCUAL MARCO MARTÍNEZ **m** *Ambassador Extraordinary & Plenipotentiary* (since 29 August 2021)
       Mrs Géraldine Anne Dufort Ravier
Mr José M. Fernández López de Turiso *Minister Counsellor, Deputy Head of Mission*
Captain (N) José Luis Nieto Fernández **m** *Defence, Naval, Army & Air Attaché*
Mr Carlos Díaz Valcárcel **m** *Consul General*
Mr Miguel Oliveros Torres *Counsellor for Cultural & Scientific Affairs*
Mrs María Cruz-Guzmán Flores *Counsellor*
Mrs Ana M. Rodríguez Pérez * *Counsellor (Press & Communications)*
Ms Soledad García López *Counsellor (Customs, Excise & Tax Affairs)*
Mr Félix Álvarez Saavedra **m** *Counsellor (Home Affairs)*
Mr Victor Jiménez Fernández * *Counsellor (Transport & Maritime Affairs)*
Mr José A. Benedicto Iruiñ **m** *Counsellor (Education)*
Mrs Blanca Cano Sánchez **m** Counsellor *(Employment & Social Affairs)*
Dr Manuel Butler Halter **m** *Counsellor (Tourism)*
Mrs Rosa M. Gómez Movellán **m** *Counsellor (Agriculture, Fisheries & Food)*
Mr Álvaro Nadal Belda **m** *Counsellor (Economic & Commercial)*
Mr Enrique López Hernando **m** *Counsellor*
Mr Nuño Bordallo Sainz **m** *Counsellor (Consular Affairs)*
Mrs Nuria González-Barros Camba *Counsellor (Political Affairs)*
Mrs Cristina Ruenes Mariñas *1st Secretary (Political Affairs)*
Mr Eduardo Escribano Martín *1st Secretary (Political Affairs)*
Mr Carlos Hugo Murillo Gómez *Counsellor (Consular Affairs)*
Mrs Mª Celia Reviriego Morales *Attaché (Home Affairs)*
Mr Juan A. Jiménez Arnedo **m** *Attaché (Home Affairs)*
Mr Andrés Galván Ramírez *Attaché (Maritime Affairs)*
Dr Esteban Pacha Vicente **m** *Attaché (Transport & Infrastructures)*
Mr Pedro Medina Asensio **m** *Deputy Counsellor (Tourism)*
Ms Maria J. Conde Solé *Attaché (Press & Communications)*
Mr Rafael Ortega Ripoll **m** *Commercial Counsellor*
Mrs Cristina Valverde García de la Barrera **m** *Attaché*
Mr Luis Álvarez Ruiz **m** *Attaché (Commercial)*
Mr José M. García Moreno *Liaison Magistrate to the UK*
Ms Beatriz Aparicio Campillo *Chancellor*

SRI LANKA

High Commission of the Democratic Socialist Republic of Sri Lanka
13 Hyde Park Gardens W2 2LU
020 7262 1841
Fax 020 7262 7970
mail@slhc-london.co.uk
www.srilankahighcommission.co.uk
Monday-Friday 09.30 -17.30

HER EXCELLENCY MRS SAROJA SIRISENA **m** *High Commissioner (since 2 March 2020)*
       Mr Sudath Parakrama Talpahewa
Mr Samantha Priyadarshana Weerasinghe Pathirana **m** *Deputy High Commissioner*
Mrs Lakmini Priyanga Peiris Mendis **m** *Minister (Trade)*
Brigadier Labunu Hewage Mahinda Rajapaksha * *Minister Counsellor (Defence)*
Mr Christy Ruban Augustin **m** *Counsellor*
Mr Hettiyakandage Arunapushpa Saumyasiri **m** *Counsellor*
Mr. Senuja Samaraweera **m** *2nd Secretary (Commerce)*
Miss Athuraliyage Thivanka Upachala *3rd Secretary*
Miss Thimuthu Sanjika Dissanayake *3rd Secretary*
Mrs Gaya Kasunmalee Senaratne **m** *3rd Secretary*

Embassy of the Republic of the Sudan
3 Cleveland Row St James's SW1A 1DD

020 7839 8080
info@sudan-embassy.co.uk
www.sudan-embassy.co.uk

HIS EXCELLENCY MR MOHAMED ABDALLA IDRIS MOHAMED **m** *Ambassador Extraordinary & Plenipotentiary* *(since 8 February 2019)*
  Mrs Rugaiya Shuaib Idris Mohamed
Brigadier Mohamed Abdelrahman Mohamed Babiker * *Military Attaché*
Mr Khalid Mohamed Ali Hassan **m** *Counsellor*
Mr Almoiz Mohammed Abdulaziz Khairy **m** *2nd Secretary*
Mr Mohamed Mustafa Karar Ahmed **m** *Counsellor*
Mr Gaffar Osman Mubarak Osman **m** *1st Secretary*
Ms Ola Omer Abdelrahman Mahmoud Elgindi **m** *3rd Secretary*
Mr Yasir Abdelazem Adam Uthman **m** *3rd Secretary*

SURINAME

Embassy of the Republic of Suriname
91 Rue du Ranelagh, 75016
Paris, FRANCE
(00) 33 01 45 25 93 00
Amb.frankrijk@gov.sr

Contact Details in the United Kingdom:
127 Pier House
31 Cheyne Walk
London SW3 5HN
(00) 44 7768 196 326
ajethu@honoraryconsul.info

HIS EXCELLENCY MR REGGY MARTIALES NELSON **m** *Ambassador Extraordinary & Plenipotentiary (since 5 July 2019)*
  Mrs Haidy Madelien Gravenberch

SWEDEN

Embassy of Sweden
11 Montagu Place W1H 2AL
Main Switchboard 020 7917 6400
Passports 020 7917 6410
Visas 020 7917 6418
Defence 020 7917 6426
Passports & Visas Fax 020 7917 6475
ambassaden.london@gov.se
www.swedenabroad.com/london
Monday-Friday 09.00-12.00

Swedish Trade and Investment Council – Business Sweden
4ᵗʰ Floor
5 Upper Montagu Street W1H 2AG
Main Switchboard: 020 7258 5130
Fax: 020 7616 4099
Email: unitedkingdom@business-sweden.se

HER EXCELLENCY MRS MIKAELA KUMLIN GRANIT **m** *Ambassador Extraordinary & Plenipotentiary (since 15 August 2021)*
  Mr Jakob Granit
Mrs Åsa Theander **m** *Minister-Counsellor (Political and European Affairs), Deputy Head of Mission*
Mrs Annika White **m** *Counsellor (Administrative & Consular Affairs)*
Ms Marleen Windahl *1st Secretary (Consular Affairs)*
Mrs Anna Brodin **m** *1st Secretary (Political Affairs)*
Mr Mikael Elmehed **m** *1st Secretary (Foreign & Security Policy)*
Mrs Louise Ritondo **m** *3rd Secretary*

Ms Pia Lundberg *Counsellor (Cultural Affairs)*
Mrs Cecilia Hivander **m** *Counsellor*
Colonel Per Appelkvist **m** *Defence Attaché*
Lieutenant Colonel Peter Viklund * *Deputy Defence Attaché*
Mr Jonas Borgefors **m** *1st Secretary*
Mr Gustaf Bergström **m** *Commercial Counsellor & Trade Commissioner*

SWITZERLAND

Embassy of Switzerland
16 -18 Montagu Place W1H 2BQ
020 7616 6000
Fax 020 7724 7001
london@eda.admin.ch
www.eda.admin.ch/london

Regional Consular Centre London
c/o Embassy of Switzerland in the United Kingdom
16-18 Montagu Place W1H 2BQ
020 7616 6000
Fax 020 7724 7001
Passport & visa section by appointment only
london.cc@eda.admin.ch
www.eda.admin.ch/rcclondon

HIS EXCELLENCY Mr Markus Leitner **m** *Ambassador Extraordinary & Plenipotentiary (since 30 July 2021)*
      Mrs Doris Karola Leitner
Ms Chantal Moser *Minister & Deputy Head of Mission*
Lieutenant Colonel Joachim Adler **m** *Defence Attaché (Military, Naval and Air Attaché)*
Mr Jean-Daniel Pitteloud **m** *Police Attaché*
Mr Marcus Rothen **m** *Counsellor (Head Economic, Finance, Science & Innovation)*
Mrs Stefanie Küng **m** *Counsellor (Deputy Head Economic, Finance, Science & Innovation)*
Mrs Manuela Ferrari **m** *Counsellor & Consul General (Head Finance, Personnel & Administration)*
Mrs Simona Regazzoni Kwenda **m** *Counsellor & Consul (Head Regional Consular Centre)*
Mr Marco Fischer *Counsellor (Head Political & Legal Affairs)*
Mr Bernhard Küffer **m** *1st Secretary (Financial & Fiscal Affairs)*
Ms Andrea Hauri *3rd Secretary (Consular Affairs)*
Mrs Marina Sidler Yüce **m** *Attaché (Visa Affairs)*

SYRIA
(Temporarily closed by the Syrian Government)
Embassy of the Syrian Arab Republic
8 Belgrave Square SW1X 8PH
020 7245 9012
Fax 020 7235 4621
www.syrianembassy.co.uk
Monday-Friday 09.30-15.30

TAJIKISTAN

Embassy of the Republic of Tajikistan
FM House, 110 Clarendon Road,
Notting Hill,
London W11 2HR
+44 (0) 20 3904 6371
tajemblondon@mfa.tj
www.tajembassy.org.uk

Her EXCELLENCY MRS RUKHSHONA EMOMALI **m** *Ambassador Extraordinary & Plenipotentiary (since 6 January 2022)*
      Mr Shamsullo Sakhibov

Mr Zafar Safarov **m** *1st Secretary & Consul*
Mr Bakhtiyor Muhamedjanov **m** *2nd Secretary*
Mr Rustam Mullodoza **m** *3rd Secretary*

TANZANIA

High Commission of the United Republic of Tanzania
3 Stratford Place
London
W1C 1AS
Tel: 02075691470
Email: tanzani@tzhc.uk
Website: www.tzhc.uk

HER EXCELLENCY DR ASHA-ROSE MIGIRO **m** *High Commissioner (since 14 June 2016)*
        Professor Cleophas MIGIRO
Brigadier General Bright Livingstone Msuya **m** *Defence Adviser*
Mr Patrick Mwakalobo **m** *Minister Plenipotentiary, Cultural & Education Affairs*
Ms Mercy Eliatosha Kitonga **m** *Minister-Counsellor, Political Affairs*
Mr Wema Ezekiel Kibona **m** *Finance Attaché*
Mr Juma Sheha **m** *Counsellor, IMO and other International Organisations*
Mr Ally Mohamed Mtanda **m** *Counsellor, Immigration Attaché*
Ms Ngusekela Karen Nyerere **m** *Counsellor, Multilateral Matters*
Mr Adam Mhagama **m** *First Secretary, Trade, Investment and Tourism*

THAILAND

Royal Thai Embassy
29-30 Queen's Gate SW7 5JB
020 7225 5500, 020 7589 2944
Fax 020 7823 9695
rtelondon@thaiembassyuk.org.uk
www.thaiembassyuk.org.uk
Monday-Friday 09.00 -12.30 & 14.00-17.00

Consular Section
Basement, 29-30 Queen's Gate SW7 5JB
020 7589 5528
Fax 020 7823 7492
csinfo@thaiembassyuk.org.uk
visa@thaiembassyuk.org.uk
Monday-Friday 09.00 -12.00

Office of the Defence & Naval Attaché
29-30 Queen's Gate SW7 5JB
020 7589 0492
Fax 020 7225 3782

Office of the Military Attaché
29-30 Queen's Gate SW7 5JB
020 7589 3155
Fax 020 7589 3155

Office of the Air Attaché
29-30 Queen's Gate SW7 5JB
020 7589 0369
Fax 020 7589 0369

Office of Commercial Affairs
11 Hertford Street W1Y 7DX
020 7493 5749
Fax 020 7493 7416

Office of Economic and Financial Affairs
29-30 Queen's Gate SW7 5JB
020 7589 7266
Fax 020 7589 2624

Office of Educational Affairs
28 Prince's Gate SW7 1QF
020 7584 4538
Fax 020 7823 9896

HIS EXCELLENCY MR PISANU SUVANAJATA m *Ambassador Extraordinary & Plenipotentiary (since March 2017)*
       Mrs Thipayasuda Suvanajata
Mrs Urasa Mongkolnavin * *Minister & Deputy Head of Mission*
Captain Jaiped Thongdoung, RTN m *Defence Attaché & Naval Attaché*
Group Captain Wisut Inkham m *Assistant Defence Attaché & Air Attaché*
Colonel Tanadej Phusipaphawong m *Assistant Defence Attaché & Military Attaché*
Miss Vatcharaporn Ratanayanont * *Minister (Education)*
Mr Nadhavudh Dhamasiri *Minister (Economic and Financial)*
Mr Prakhan Kordumrong m *Minister (Commercial)*
Mr Srunyu Ampartrakarn m *Minister-Counsellor & Head of Chancery*
Mr Watchara Chiemanukulkit m *Minister-Counsellor (Maritime)*
Miss Chompunuch Piyawatwichit *Minister-Counsellor*
Captain Lertrob Sirirak, RTN m *Assistant Defence Attaché & Assistant Naval Attaché*
Mrs Premruedee Lotharukpong * *Counsellor (Information)*
Miss Lasapan Toomsawasdi *Counsellor (Consular)*
Mr Chatchavarn Watanakhiri m *Counsellor (Political and Economic)*
Mr Kitti-Chanok Phaholyothin m *Counsellor (Protocol)*
Miss Kanyalak Cheeravinij m *Counsellor (International Organisations)*
Miss Chalermwan Jariyanapiwart *Counsellor (Commercial)*
Mr Pacharapol Padermprach *1st Secretary (Consular)*
Mrs Jesada Imprasertsuk *2nd Secretary (Administrative)*
Miss Uraiwan Padsri *3rd Secretary (Administrative)*

TIMOR-LESTE

Embassy of the Democratic Republic of Timor-Leste
6th Floor, 83 Victoria Street, London SW1H 0HW
020 3585 4062 – 020 3585 4063
info@tlembassy.co.uk

Vacant
Mrs Melania Nurlina
Mr Gilson da Carvalho Ramos da Silva *Counsellor / Chargé d' Affaires a.i*
Mrs Sandra Fatima Castro Rego Ximenes * *Second Secretary*

TOGO

Embassy of the Republic of Togo
Unit 3, 7 & 8 Lysander Mews
Lysander Grove, London
N19 3QP
020 72637522
Monday-Friday 09.00-13.00 & 14.00-17.00

Vacant *Ambassador Extraordinary & Plenipotentiary*
Mr Komlavi Dedji *Minister-Counsellor Chargé d'Affaires a. i.*
Mr Kokou Dokodzo m *Counsellor (Financial)*
Mr Dzidzoe Megnimabou Mensah m *Economic Adviser*
Mr Kpalete Agossou Kpade m *1st Secretary*
Mr Ankou Gadjekpo m *Consular Attaché*
Mr Bona Henri Doufodji m *Administration Attaché*

TONGA

Tonga High Commission
36 Molyneux Street W1H 5BQ
020 7724 5828
Fax 020 7723 9074
Monday-Friday 09.00-13.00 & 14.00-17.00

HER EXCELLENCY HON MRS TITILUPE FANETUPOUVAVAU TUIVAKANO **m** *High Commissioner (since 28 May 2018)*
        Major Siaosi Kiu Kaho
Mr Viliami Fonongaloa Lolohea * *1st Secretary*

TRINIDAD & TOBAGO

High Commission of the Republic of Trinidad & Tobago
42 Belgrave Square SW1X 8NT
020 7245 9351 Fax 020 7823 1065
hclondon@foreign.gov.tt
http://foreign.gov.tt/hclondon
Monday-Friday 09.00-17.00

HIS EXCELLENCY MR VISHNU DHANPAUL **m** *High Commissioner (since 21 October 2021)*
        Mrs Anastasia Geofroy-Dhanpaul
Ms Jenny G Thompson *Counsellor*
Ms Kimberly A Ibrahim *2nd Secretary*
Ms Helena Jackson **m** *Immigration Attaché*
Mrs Alicia Acres-Youksee **m** *Immigration Attaché*

TUNISIA

Embassy of Tunisia
29 Prince's Gate SW7 1QG
020 7584 8117
Fax 020 7584 3205
London@tunisianembassy.co.uk
www.at-londres.diplomatie.gov.tn

Military Attaché's Office
Tel/Fax: 020 7581 0952
dmlondres@defense.tn

HIS EXCELLENCY MR NABIL BEN KHEDHER * *Ambassador Extraordinary & Plenipotentiary(since 30 September 2017)*
        Mrs Maha Ben Larbi
Mr Wassim Hajeri **m** *Minister Plenipotentiary*
Mrs Nour Zarrouk EP Boumiza **m** *Counsellor*
Mr Khiareddine Daboussi **m** *Counsellor*
Mr Kadri Mahmoudi **m** *Counsellor*
Senior Col. Mourad Kouki **m** *Military Naval & Air Attaché*
Captain Mondher Chakroun **m** *Deputy Military,Naval and Air Attaché*
Mr Cherif Nouicer **m** *Counsellor*
Mr Amara Hosni **m** *Counsellor*
Mr Rafik Ben Henia **m** *third Secretary*
Mr Mohamed Hichem Sahraoui **m** *Attaché (Consular Section)*
Mrs Karima Boughattas * *Attaché (Counsular Section)*
Mr Taha Chaabane * *Attaché (Counsular Section)*
Mr Chedli Khlifi * *Attaché (Military Section)*
Mr Mohsen Khiari * *Attaché*

TURKEY

Embassy of the Republic of Turkey
43 Belgrave Square SW1X 8PA
020 7393 0202
Fax 020 7393 0066
embassy.london@mfa.gov.tr
london.emb.mfa.gov.tr

Ambassador's Office
020 7393 0222
Fax 020 7393 9213

Military Attaché's Office
020 7235 6862
asat.londra@tsk.tr

Legal Counsellor's Office
020 7201 7046

Press Counsellor's Office
020 7235 6968
londra@iletisim.gov.tr

Religious Affairs Counsellor's Office
020 8340 5500
ingilterediyanet@gmail.com

Educational Counsellor's Office
020 3915 4541
londra@meb.gov.tr

Cultural & Information Counsellor's Office
020 7839 7778
info@gototurkey.co.uk

Treasury & Financial Counsellor's Office
020 7245 0434
hmlondon@hazine.gov.tr

Commercial Counsellor's Office
020 7838 9167
londra@ticaret.gov.tr

Central Bank of the Republic of Turkey Representative Office
020 7220 9590
cbtlondon@btconnect.com

Consulate General of the Republic of Turkey
Rutland Lodge Rutland Gardens Knightsbridge SW7 1BW
020 7591 6900
Fax 020 7591 6911
consulate.london@mfa.gov.tr
london.cg.mfa.gov.tr

HIS EXCELLENCY MR ÜMİT YALÇIN m *Ambassador Extraordinary & Plenipotentiary (since 27 September 2018)*
        Mrs Gül Yalçın
Mr Güneş Yeşildağ m *1st Counsellor (Political Officer), Deputy Head of Mission*
Mr Bekir Utku Atahan m *Consul General*
Col Ömür Candar m *Defence & Army Attaché*
Capt Birol Sütçuoğlu m *Naval Attaché*
Col Serkan Virlan m *Air Attaché*
Mr Umut İlhan Durmuşoğlu m *Justice Counsellor*

Mr Kemal Şahin **m** *Counsellor for Security Cooperation & Interior Affairs*
Mr Mustafa Erdem **m** *Counsellor for Security Cooperation & Interior Affairs*
Mr Hacı Hasan Murat Özsoy **m** *Chief Commercial Counsellor*
Mr Tarık Sönmez **m** *Chief Commercial Counsellor*
Mr Ensari Yentürk **m** *Counsellor for Religious Affairs*
Mr Hasan Ünsal **m** *Education Counsellor*
Mr Orhan Kandar **m** *Economic Counsellor*
Mr Erdal Yılmaz **m** *Economic Counsellor*
Mrs Fatma Pınar Erdem Küçükbıçakcı **m** *Counsellor for Treasury & Financial Affairs*
Mrs Arzu Kahraman Yılmaz **m** *Counsellor for Cultural & Information Affairs*
Mrs Sezin Şahin Yeşildağ **m** *Counsellor (Political Officer)*
Mrs Ceren Serbest **m** *Counsellor (Political Officer)*
Mrs Hatice Özge Demirkurt Atahan **m** *Counsellor (Political Officer)*
Mr Özkan Serbest **m** *Counsellor (Political Officer)*
Mr Selçuk Özcan **m** *Counsellor (Political Officer)*
Mr Özgür Bora Özkul *Counsellor (Political Officer)*
Mrs Işınsu Topcuoğlu **m** *Vice Consul General*
Mr Hakan Etkin **m** *Vice Consul General*
Mrs Gül Etkin **m** *Counsellor*
Mr Levent Çeri **m** *Counsellor*
Mr Mehmet Hanifi Güler *Maritime Counsellor*
Mr Selçuk Gedikli **m** *2nd Secretary (Political Officer)*
Mr Ahmet Rasim Akan *2nd Secretary (Political Officer)*
Mr Nevzat Cengiz **m** *2nd Secretary*
Mr Seyfettin Doğru *3rd Secretary (Political Officer)*
Mrs Tuğba Küçükali Gedikli **m** *Attaché*
Mr Ahmet Ünal **m** *Attaché*
NCO Hasan Yoluç **m** *Military Administrative Attaché*
Mr Serhat Öntürk **m** *Attaché*
Mr Tuncay Can *Attaché*
Mr Mehmet Serdar Ercan **m** *Attaché*
Mr Murat Kılıçkaya **m** *Attaché*
Mr Sabri Doğan **m** *Attaché*
Mr Mete Dilman **m** *Attaché*
Mr Birkan Temeş **m** *Attaché*
Mrs Fatma Arslan **m** *Attaché*
Mr Ogün Sedat Öztürk **m** *Attaché*
Mr İlhan Yaşar Kaya **m** *Attaché*

TURKMENISTAN

Embassy of Turkmenistan
131 Holland Park Avenue W11 4UT
020 7610 5239
Fax 020 7751 1903
Monday-Friday 09.30-18.00
Consular Section Monday-Friday 10.00-12.00 & 14.00-16.00 (Closed Wednesday)
tkm-embassy-uk@btconnect.com
uk.tmembassy.gov.tm

HIS EXCELLENCY MR YAZMURAD N. SERYAEV **m** *Ambassador Extraordinary & Plenipotentiary (since 02 July 2003)*
     Mrs Djennetgozel Seryaeva
Mr Dovlet Atabayev **m** *Counsellor*
Mrs Oguljahan Atabayeva **m** *1st Secretary*
Mr Bayramgeldi Nepesov **m** *1st Secretary/Consul*
Mr Umyt Ovezov **m** *3rd Secretary*

TUVALU

London Honorary Consulate (see Honorary Consuls section below)

UGANDA

Uganda High Commission
Uganda House 58-59 Trafalgar Square WC2N 5DX
020 7839 5783
Fax 020 7839 8925
info@ugandahighcomission.co.uk; admin@ugandahighcomission.co.uk
www.ugandahighcommission.co.uk

HIS EXCELLENCY MR JULIUS PETER MOTO m *High Commissioner (Since 30 August 2017)*
      Mrs Eunice Abeja Moto
Mr John Leonard Mugerwa m *Deputy High Commissioner*
Mr Godfrey Kwoba m *Minister-Counsellor (Commercial & Economic matters)*
Mr Robert Basiima m *Counsellor*
Mrs Juliet Namiiro Mugerwa m *Counsellor (Head of Consular)*
Ms Miriam Otengo *Counsellor (Commercial & Economic Affairs)*
Brigadier General James Kaija m *Defence Adviser*
Ms Jackie Kemirembe *3rd Secretary (Trade, Investment & Tourism)*
Mr Brian Ssekyewa *3rd Secretary (Protocol, Public Diplomacy & Education)*

UKRAINE

Embassy of Ukraine
60 Holland Park W11 3SJ
020 7727 6312
Fax 020 7792 1708
emb_gb@mfa.gov.ua
http://uk.mfa.gov.ua/en

Monday-Friday 09.00-13.00 & 14.00-18.00

Ambassador's Office
60 Holland Park W11 3SJ
020 7727 6312
Fax 020 7792 1708
tetiana.tokarska@mfa.gov.ua

Economic Section
60 Holland Park W11 3SJ
020 7727 6312
Fax 020 7792 1708
economy@ukremb.org.uk

Consular and Visa Section
78 Kensington Park Road W11 2PL
Tel 020 7243 8923 (Monday – Friday: 9.30 am to 1.00 pm)
Fax 020 7727 3567
consul_gb@mfa.gov.ua
Hours of Service: Monday, Tuesday, Thursday, Friday 10.00 am - 1.00 pm
Wednesday 1.00 pm - 4:30 pm

HIS EXCELLENCY MR VADYM PRYSTAIKO m *Ambassador Extraordinary & Plenipotentiary (since 2 September 2020)* Mrs Inna Prystaiko spouse

Mr Andriy Marchenko m *Minister-Counsellor*
Mr Taras Krykun m *Minister-Counsellor (Economic Affairs)*
Mr Yevgen Lisuchenko m Counsellor (Political Affairs)
(Deputy Permanent Representative of Ukraine to the IMO)
Mr Vitallii Borovko m Counsellor (Political Affaires)
Mr Dmytro Tretiakov m *1st Secretary (Political Affairs)*
Mr Volodymyr Pavlichenko m *1st Secretary (Political Affairs)*
Mr Valentyn Maksymchuk m *1st Secretary (Trade & Economic Affairs)*
Mr Mykola Dzhygun m *1st Secretary (Consular Affairs)*

Ms Alisa Lialina *1st Secretary*
Captain (N) Dmytro Donskoi Defense and Air Attaché
Colonel Vitalii Kraskovkyi Military Attaché
Commander Oleksii Fedchenko, Naval Attaché
Ms Valeriia Budakova *Third Secretary on Legal Affairs*
Ms Tetiana Tokarska *Second Secretary, Assistant to the Ambassador*
Mr Volodymyr Kolesnyk **m** Third Secretary (Consular Affairs)
Mr Serhii Bondarenko **m** Third Secretary

UNITED ARAB EMIRATES

Embassy of the United Arab Emirates
1 - 2 Grosvenor Crescent London SW1X 7EE
020 7581 1281
Fax 0207 808381
https://www.mofaic.gov.ae/en/missions/london

Consular Section
48 Prince's Gate, London SW7 2QA
020 7808 8301
Fax 020 7584 0989

Cultural Attaché Office
48 Prince's Gate, London SW7 2QA
02078088318
Fax 020 7581 1870

Police Attaché Office
48 Prince's Gate, London SW7 2QA
020 7808 8337
Fax 020 7823 7716

Military Attaché Office
6 Queen's Gate Terrace, London SW7 5PF
020 7581 4113
Fax 020 7589 9120

Medical Attaché Office
71 Harley Street, London W1G 8DE
020 7486 6281
Fax 020 7224 3575

HIS EXCELLENCY MR MANSOOR ABDULLAH KHALFAN JUMA ABULHOUL **m** *Ambassador Extraordinary &*
Plenipotentiary
Mrs Victoria Maria Elisabeth Béatrice Devin
Miss Rawdha Mohamed Jumaa Mohamed Alotaiba *Deputy Head of Mission*
Mr Hassan Mohammad Murad Mohammad Almazmi **m** *Counsellor & Head of Finance and Administrative Affairs*
Mr Khaldoon Khalifa Alshaikhahmad Almubarak * *Counsellor (Economic)*
Mr Marwan Ahmed Abdelrazaq Abdalla Alnaqbi **m** *2nd Secretary & Head of Economic Affairs*
Mr Ahmed Khalid Mohammed Abdulla Alabdooli *3rd Secretary & Head of Political Affairs*
Mr Ahmed Awad Sultan Balghamisa Alshamsi *Attaché (Political)*
Mr Sohail Mohamed Ali Almulla Alrayssi * *3rd Secretary & Head of Consular Affairs*
Mr Husain Mohamed Omar Saeed Al Meer * *Administrative Attaché*
Mr Buti Saeed Salem Saeed Alsubousi **m** *Military Attaché*
Mr Ali Salem Rashed Humaid Alkaabi * *Assistant Military Attaché*
Mr Khaled Khamis Rashed Hasan Alghafri * *Assistant Military Attaché*
Mr Mohammed Abdulla Mohammed Arar Aldhaheri * *Assistant Military Attaché*
Mr Humaid Khalifa Mohamed Thani Alremeithi * *Assistant Military Attaché*
Mr Rashed Abdulla Mohammed Khuwaidem Alneyadi * *Assistant Military Attaché*
Mr Abdelaziz Ahmed Obaid Ahmed Alkindi * *Assistant Military Attaché*

Lt Col Abdulrahman Jasem Salem Rubayea Aldhaheri **m** *Police Attaché*
Mr Saif Nasser Ali Nasser Alsaedi **m** *Deputy Police Attaché*
Mr Salem Shehail Salem Saeed Alsaedi **m** *Assistant Police Attaché*
Mr Jamal Abdulaziz Nasser Alowais **m** *Medical Attaché*
Mrs Simi Anna Solomon **m** *Assistant Medical Attaché*
Mr Abdulla Musabbeh Khalfan Musabbeh Alkaabi * *Cultural Attaché*
Ms Roudha Ahmad Ibrahim Aldowais Alshamsi *Administrative Attaché (Cultural Attaché Office)*
Mr Hamad Homood Sulaiman Ali Alebri **m** *Administrative Attaché (Cultural Attaché Office)*
Mr Mohammed Ibrahim A Alshaibani **m** *Attaché*
Mr Abdulla Saeed Bin Nasser Al Mansoori *Administrative Attaché*
Mr Mohammed Atiq Abdulla Burgaiba Alzarooni **m** *Administrative Attaché*
Mr Sultan Ali Sultan Hilal Alsuboosi **m** *Attaché*
Shaikh Hamdan Bin Maktoum Bin Rashed Bin Saeed Al-Maktoum *3rd Secretary*
Mr Saif Saeed Mohammed Balbadi Aldhaheri **m** *Counsellor*

UNITED STATES OF AMERICA

U.S. Embassy London
33 Nine Elms Lane, London SW11 7US
020 77499 9000
Monday-Friday 0830-1730

Vacant *Ambassador Extraordinary & Plenipotentiary*
Mr Philip Thomas Reeker **m** Chargé d'Affaires, ai
Ms Caryn McClelland *Minister-Counsellor (Economic Affairs)*
Mr Frank Ledahawsky **m** *Minister-Counsellor (Management Affairs)*
Mr Joseph Pennington **m** *Minister Counsellor (Political Affairs)*
Ms Meredith McEvoy **m** *Minister Counsellor (Consular Affairs)*
Ms Kathryn Crockart **m** *Minister Counsellor (Public Affairs)*
Ms Rosemary Gallant **m** *Minister Counsellor (Commercial Affairs)*
Ms Karen Lass *Counsellor of Embassy (Regional Security Affairs)*
Mr John Schutte **m** *Counsellor of Embassy (Economic Affairs)*
Ms Lisa Brodey **m** *Counsellor*
Mr Jason Donovan **m** *Counsellor*
Mr James Crawford **m** *Counsellor of Embassy (Medical Affairs)*
Mr Michael Driscoll **m** *Counsellor of Embassy (Coordination Affairs)*
Ms Cynthia Guven **m** *Counsellor of Embassy (Agricultural Affairs)*
Mr John Cloutier **m** *Counsellor (Political Affairs)*
Mr Richard Hoch **m** *Counsellor*
Mr Jason Stock **m** *Counsellor*
Brig Gen Jefferson O'Donnell **m** *Defense Attaché*
Capt Kevin Quarderer **m** *Naval Attaché*
Col Charles Metrolis **m** *Air Force Attaché*
Col Michael Cullinane *Army Attaché*
Lt Col Adam Lefringhouse **m** *Marine Attaché*
Mr Robert Friedenberg **m** *Attaché*
Mr Craig Symons **m** *Attaché*
Ms Sheila Thomas **m** *Attaché*
Mr Stephen Cyrus **m** *Legal Attaché*
Ms Jennifer Schroeder-Fawcett **m** *Attaché*
Mr James Griffin **m** *Attaché*
Col William Courtemanche **m** *Attaché*
Mr Russell Roth **m** *Attaché*
Ms Haley Gallagher **m** *Attaché*
Mr Matthew Coats **m** *Attaché*
Ms Vanessa Sisti *Attaché*
Mr Kenneth Kohl **m** *Attaché*
Ms Angela Stubblefield **m** *Attaché*

Mr Anthony Cook m *Attaché*
Mr James Erwin m *Attaché*
Ms Margaret Kane *First Secretary*
Mr Adam Boyd m *Attaché*
Mr Max Schindler m *First Secretary*
Ms Ginger Campbell *First Secretary*
Mr Kevin Rubesh m *Attaché*
Mr Eugene West m *First Secretary*
Mr Aaron Snipe m *First Secretary*
Mr Damon Trent Dabney m *Attaché*
Mr Peter Chordas m *Attaché*
Mr Jose Tobias m *First Secretary*
Mr Jon Schwerdtfeger m *Attaché*
Mr Carson Wu m *First Secretary - Consul*
Mr Stanislas Parmentier m *First Secretary*
Ms Linda Fenton m *First Secretary*
Ms Diane Parsont m *First Secretary*
Mr John Mahr m *First Secretary*
Mr Luis Martinez m *Attaché*
Ms Christina Tribble m *First Secretary*
Mr Douglas Haidle m *Attaché*
Mr Christopher Jones *First Secretary*
Ms Shari Berke m *First Secretary*
Ms Debra Fertig m *Attaché*
Ms Brenda VanHorn *First Secretary*
Mr Guy Lawson m *First Secretary*
Mr Marshall Derks *First Secretary - Consul*
Ms Joslyn Mack-Wilson m *First Secretary*
Mr Jeffrey Hay m *First Secretary*
Mr Matthew Singer m *First Secretary*
Mr Jamal Jafari m *First Secretary*
Ms Rita Rico m *First Secretary*
Mr Jay Porter m *First Secretary*
Mr Eric Vanderstelt m *Attaché*
Mr Brett Eggleston m *First Secretary*
Mr Roland Mckay m *First Secretary*
Mr Robert Tibbetts m *First Secretary*
Mr Todd Wilder m *First Secretary - Consul*
Ms Lisa Petzold *First Secretary*
Mr Jeffrey Moffatt m *First Secretary*
Mr Christiaan James m *First Secretary*
Ms Rebecca Klug m *First Secretary*
Ms Janelle Weyek m *First Secretary*
Ms Kimberly Ofobike m *First Secretary*
Mr Jason Petty m *First Secretary*
Ms Lynne Radcliffe *First Secretary*
Ms Ankita Perry m *First Secretary*
Mr Jeremy Kinsell m *First Secretary*
Ms Kate Addison m *First Secretary*
Mr Matt Rumfelt m *First Secretary*
Mr Adam Nielson m *First Secretary*
Mr Andrew Daehne *First Secretary*
Mr Humza Tarar m *First Secretary*
Ms Clarissa Adamson m *Second Secretary Consul*
Ms Marija Canic m *Second Secretary*
Mr Seann Gale *Second Secretary*
Ms Caroline Widegren m *Second Secretary*
Ms Kathy Wang Yao *Attaché*
Ms Anna Kearl *Second Secretary*
Mr Jeffrey Vanoverbeke m *Second Secretary*
Ms Cassandra Hagar *Second Secretary - Consul*
Mr Jeremy Wisemiller m *Second Secretary - Consul*

Ms Anne Vasquez **m** *Second Secretary - Consul*
Ms Bridget Blagoevski-Trazoff **m** *Second Secretary*
Mr Mark Bridges **m** *Attaché*
Mr Ross Wichard **m** *Attaché*
Mr Victor Bernard **m** *Second Secretary*
Mr Robert Mann **m** *Second Secretary*
Ms Julie Curry *Second Secretary*
Ms Mona Martineau **m** *Second Secretary*
Mr Robert Baldridge *Second Secretary*
Mr Eric Adler **m** *Second Secretary*
Ms Cristina Busacca **m** *Second Secretary*
Mr Michael Jesada **m** *Second Secretary*
Ms Claire Quirke **m** *Second Secretary*
Mr Richard Hatch **m** *Second Secretary*
Ms Katrina Barnas *Second Secretary - Vice Consul*
Ms Brigitta Sajcic *Second Secretary*
Mr Edward Shin **m** *Second Secretary - Vice Consul*
Mr Jason Hammontree **m** *Second Secretary*
Mr Sydney Smith *Second Secretary*
Mr Christopher Leonetti **m** *Second Secretary*
Mr William Lagana **m** *Second Secretary*
Mr Newell Timothy **m** *Second Secretary*
Mr Chad Lamb **m** *Second Secretary*
Ms Tamika Jeffries *Second Secretary*
Mr Adrian York **m** *Attaché*
Ms Christine Kelley **m** *Second Secretary*
Ms Linda Shin **m** *Second Secretary - Vice Consul*
Ms Christine Dwulet **m** *Second Secretary - Vice Consul*
Mr Andrew Abordonado *Second Secretary - Vice Consul*
Mr Paily Eapen **m** *Second Secretary - Vice Consul*
Ms Willow Williamson **m** *Second Secretary - Vice Consul*
Mr Nicholas Jager **m** *Second Secretary - Vice Consul*
Mr Wesley Fredericks **m** *Second Secretary*
Ms Lindsey Bowman *Second Secretary - Vice Consul*
Mr Nabil Flowers **m** *Second Secretary - Vice Consul*
Ms Shiva Marvasti *Second Secretary - Consul*
Mr Maciej Luczywo *Second Secretary - Consul*
Mr Theodore Vastine **m** *Second Secretary*
Mr Christopher Ricci *Second Secretary*
Mr Kenneth Van Wyck **m** *Second Secretary*
Ms Whitney Bryce Kincaid *Attaché - Vice Consul*
Ms Sara Chan **m** *Second Secretary*
Mr Matthew Brown **m** *Second Secretary*
Ms Courtney Harris **m** *Second Secretary*
Mr Jeremy Branson **m** *Second Secretary*
Mr Justin Busacca **m** *Second Secretary*
Mr Ashwin Bijanki **m** *Second Secretary*
Mr James Henderson **m** *Second Secretary*
Mr Darrell Metzger **m** *Second Secretary*
Mr James Phelps **m** *Second Secretary*
Mr John Bonds **m** *Second Secretary - Vice Consul*
Ms Sarah Ancas **m** *Second Secretary - Vice Consul*
Ms Amanda Nelson-Duac **m** *Second Secretary - Vice Consul*
Mr Rafi Haroutunian **m** *Second Secretary*
Ms Siri Roma **m** *Second Secretary*
Mr Matthew Schreck **m** *Second Secretary - Vice Consul*
Mr Christopher Cramer **m** *Second Secretary - Vice Consul*
Ms Minh Tokuyama **m** *Second Secretary - Vice Consul*
Mr Mark Mock *Second Secretary - Vice Consul*
Ms Olivia Goodman *Second Secretary*
Ms Anastassia Bogosian *Second Secretary*
Ms Anastassia Bogosian-Scissors *Second Secretary*

Mr John Steele *Second Secretary - Vice Consul*
Mr David Mackey **m** *Deputy Legal Attaché*
Mr Jensen Penalosa **m** *Deputy Attaché*
Mr Lucian Martinez **s** *Attaché*
Lt Col Anthony Mims **m** *Attaché*
Mr Cory Jenkins **m** *Attaché*
Ms Ginger Miller **m** *Attaché*
Lt Col Thomas J Graham **m** *Assistant Air Attaché*
Mr Jason Johnson **m** *Assistant Legal Attaché*
Mr Matthew Johnson **m** *Assistant Legal Attaché*
Ms Stefanie Roddy **m** *Assistant Legal Attaché*
Mr Brett Graham **m** *Assistant Attaché*
Mr John Illia **m** *Assistant Attaché*
Mr Nicholas Wadding **m** *Assistant Attaché*
Mr Eric Smithmier **m** *Assistant Legal Attaché*
Mr Timothy Hemker **m** *Attaché*
Mr Luis Perez **m** *Attaché*
Mr Kerry Evans **m** *Assistant Attaché*
Mr Daniel Romanzo **m** *Assistant Attaché*
Mr Christopher Frazier **m** *Assistant Attaché*
Ms Wanda Mizell *Assistant Attaché*
Mr John Cunningham **m** *Assistant Attaché*
Mr Scott Stachowski **m** *Assistant Attaché*
MAJ David Hernandez **m** *Assistant Attaché*
CDR Neal Garbett **m** *Assistant Attaché*
Mr Christopher Larsen **m** *Assistant Attaché*
Mr Brian Lewis **m** *Assistant Attaché*
Mr Samuel Storrer **m** *Assistant Attaché*
Mr Andrew Shealy **m** *Assistant Attaché*
Ms Lindsay Bosso **m** *Assistant Attaché*
Mr Albert Cabrelli **m** *Assistant Attaché*
Mr Charles Jackson **m** *Assistant Attaché*
Mr Trent Hoover **m** *Assistant Attaché*
Mr Eric Clark **m** *Assistant Attaché*
Mr Michael Murphy **m** *Assistant Attaché*
Mr Charles Hanners **m** *Assistant Attaché*
Mr Nicholas Wadding **m** *Assistant Attaché*
Mr Andres Albarran *Assistant Attaché-Vice Consul*
Ms Abigayle Yocom **m** *Third Secretary*
Mr Joe Rodriguez *Third Secretary*
Ms Valli Chidambaram *Third Secretary - Vice Consul*
Ms Bianca Uribe **m** *Third Secretary - Vice Consul*

URUGUAY

Embassy of Uruguay
150 Brompton Road SW3 1HX
020 7584 4200
urureinounido@mrree.gub.uy
cdlondres@mrree.gub.uy

HIS EXCELLENCY MR CESAR ENEAS RODRIGUEZ ZAVALLA *Ambassador Extraordinary & Plenipotentiary*
(since 6 September 2020)
    Mrs Maria Angelica Algorta Carrau
Mrs Silvana Graciela Lesca Barolin *Minister Counsellor*
Mr Daniel Mauricio Maresca Boragno *2nd Secretary, Head of Consular Section*
Captain Guillermo Marcelo Etchevers Cazeaux **m** *Defence Attaché*

UZBEKISTAN

Embassy of the Republic of Uzbekistan
41 Holland Park W11 3RP
020 7229 7679
Fax 020 7229 7029
info@uzembassy.uk
www.uzembassy.uk

Ambassador's Office
020 7229 7679 (ext.2)

Political Affairs
020 7229 7679 (ext.3)

Trade & Investment
020 7229 7679 (ext.4)

Culture & Education
020 7229 7679 (ext.6)

Consular Section
020 7229 7679 (ext.1)
08714681100
Monday, Wednesday & Thursday 09.30-13.00
Friday 09.30-13.00, 15.00-18.00

Administrative Section
020 7229 7679 (ext.8)

Financial Section
020 7229 7679 (ext.7)

HIS EXCELLENCY MR SAID RUSTAMOV *Ambassador Extraordinary & Plenipotentiary (since 8 October 2019)*
    Mrs Diana Rustamova
Mr Aliyor Tilavov **m** *Counsellor (Political Affairs)*
Mr Ravshanbek Duschanov **m** *1st Secretary (Head of Trade & Investment)*
Mr Sultanbek Imamov **m** *1st Secretary (Consular Section)*
Mr Shokhruz Samadov **m** *Attaché*

VANUATU

Embassy of Vanuatu
Avenue de Tervueren 380 Chemin de Ronde 1150 Brussels BELGIUM
Tel/Fax: 0032 2 771 74 94
info@vanuatuembassy.be

London Honorary Consulate (see Honorary Consuls section below)

Vacant *High Commissioner*

VENEZUELA

Embassy of the Bolivarian Republic of Venezuela
1 Cromwell Road SW7 2HW
020 7584 4206 or 020 7581 2776
Fax 020 7589 8887
ambassador@venezlon.co.uk
reinounido.embajada.gob.ve

Consular Section
56 Grafton Way W1T 5DL
020 7387 6727
Fax 020 7387 2979

Defence Attaché's Office
54 Grafton Way W1T 5DL
020 7387 0695
Fax 020 7916 1155

Cultural Section
52 & 58 Grafton Way W1T 5DJ
020 7388 5788
Fax 020 7383 4857

HER EXCELLENCY MRS ROCÍO MANEIRO *Ambassador Extraordinary & Plenipotentiary (since 20 November 2014)*
Mrs Yaiza Piñate **m** *Counsellor (Consular Affairs)*
Ms Silvia Aular Soto **m** *Counsellor (Economic and Energy Affairs)*
Ms Helena Menéndez *Counsellor (Press)*
Ms María Cecilia Toro *Counsellor Counsellor (Protocol Affairs)*
Mr Heli Pulgar *Counsellor (Consular Affairs)*
Vice Admiral Elsa Iliana Guierrez Graffe *IMO*
Mr Marcos García **m** *1st Secretary*
Ms Petra Ibarra *1st Secretary*
Ms Celina Hernández *2nd Secretary*

VIET NAM

Embassy of the Socialist Republic of Viet Nam
12-14 Victoria Road W8 5RD
020 7937 1912
Fax 020 7937 6108
officeldn@vietnamembassy.org.uk
www.vietnamembassy.org.uk

Commercial Section
108 Campden Hill Road W8 7AR
020 3524 1732
thuyngh@moit.gov.vn / thuynhwork@gmail.com

HIS EXCELLENCY MR HOANG LONG NGUYEN **m** *Ambassador (since 09 June 2021)*
Mrs Huong Giang Vu
Mrs Lan-Anh Thi Nguyen * *Deputy Chief of Mission and Minister Counsellor*
Mr Van Hanh Hoang **m** *Counsellor*
Mr Coung Nguyen Canh **m** *Trade Counsellor*
Mrs Huong Ly Tran * *1st Secretary (Education)*
Mr Hoang Nam Son Bui * *1st Secretary (Political)*
Mr Quang Dong Nguyen * *2nd Secretary (Consular)*
Ms Ngoc Khanh Nguyen Bui **m** 1st *Secretary (Attaché)*
Mrs Be Thi Ut Nguyen **m** 1st *Secretary*
Mr Quoc Hai Nguyen * 2nd *Secretary*
Mr Thanh Van Vo **m** *Defence Attaché*
Mr Dinh Chien Nguyen **m** *Deputy Defence Attaché*
Mrs Van Thanh Hoang **m** *3rd Secretary(Political)*
Mrs Thuy Hong Thi Nguyen **m** *Counsellor (Commercial)*
Mr Huy Pham **m** *Attaché (Commercial)*

YEMEN

Embassy of the Republic of Yemen
57 Cromwell Road SW7 2ED
020 7584 6607
Fax 020 7589 3350
admin@yemenembassy.co.uk
Monday-Friday 09.30-16.00

HIS EXCELLENCY DR YASSIN SAEED NOMAN Ahmed m *Ambassador (since 26 June 2015)*
    Mrs Nadhirah Ali Ali Sowileh
Mr Abdullah Mohamed Abdullah Al-Jaboby m *Minister Plenipotentiary, Deputy Head of Mission*
Mr Abdulkader Ahmed Saeed Alsubeihi m *Minister Plenipotentiary*
Mr Husam Abdulhabib Saif Al-Sharjabi m *Adviser*
Mr Ali Abdullah Abbas Zabara m *Counsellor*
Mr Ahmed Mohammed Ahmed Al-Bably m *Counsellor*
Mrs Fatmah Mahmood Mohammed Afarah m *Counsellor*
Mrs Raydan Sultan NajiNaji * *Counsellor*
Mr Badr Salem Mohasen Al-Dawali *Second Secretary*

ZAMBIA

High Commission for the Republic of Zambia
Zambia House
2 Palace Gate W8 5NG
020 7581 2142
info@zambiahc.org.uk
www.zambiahc.org.uk
Monday-Friday 09.30-13.00 & 14.00-17.00

Immigration Office
020 7589 6655

HIS EXCELLENCY LT GEN PAUL MIHOVA *m* *High Commissioner (since 10 December 2019)*
    Mrs Christine Chiyesu Mihova
Ms Patricia Sikaala Chanda m *Deputy High Commissioner*
Mr Mwendabai Mataa m *Counsellor-Political*
Mr Mukela Mutukwa m *Counsellor (Economic)*
Brigadier General David Mwanza m *Defence Advisor*
Mrs Fanny Kalebwe m *1st Secretary (Finance)*
Mr Portpher Sakala m *1st Secretary (Consular)*
Ms Alice Mubanga Mulenga Shanshima *1st Secretary (Immigration)*
Mr Donald Chamoto Pelekamoyo m *1st Secretary (Tourism)*
Mr Liboma Lipalile m *1st Secretary (Protocol)*
Mrs Abigail Chaponda m *1st Secretary (Press)*
Mr Austin Kaluba m *1st Secretary (Political & Administration)*
Mr Clement Phiri m *1st Secretary (Trade)*
Mrs Rebecca Phiri m *2nd Secretary (PA to the High Commissioner)*

ZIMBABWE

Embassy of the Republic of Zimbabwe
Zimbabwe House 429 Strand WC2R 0JR
020 7836 7755
zimlondon@zimfa.gov.zw
zimembassy@zimlondon.gov.zw
http://www.zimlondon.gov.zw
Monday-Friday 09.00-13.00 & 14.00–17.00

Consular Section:
Monday-Friday 10.00–14.00

HIS EXCELLENCY COLONEL CHRISTIAN KATSANDE Ambassador Extraordinary & Plenipotentiary (since 25 June2018)
    Mrs Sophia Katsande
Mr Elisha Karodza m *Deputy Head of Mission/Minister Counsellor*
Mrs Nyarai B Mashavave m *Counsellor*
Colonel Sternford Kufa m *Defence Attaché*
Mr Chamboko Gibson T m Minister *Counsellor*
Mr Andrew Taka m *Consular Attaché*

Ms Tendai J. Chimbandi **m** *Counsellor*
Miss Hilda Madanhi *Counsellor*
Mr Oliver Mukwena **m** *Counsellor*
Mrs Evelyn Y Kufazvineyi **m** *2nd Secretary*
Ms Concilia Kwesha *3rd Secretary*

LIST OF THE REPRESENTATIVES
IN LONDON OF FOREIGN STATES &
COMMONWEALTH COUNTRIES

MBASSADORS AND HIGH COMMISSIONERS

TE	COUNTRY	HEAD OF MISSION	ROLE	RESIDENCE
/04/1993	Kuwait	Mr Khaled Al Duwaisan GCVO	Dean & Ambassador	London
/04/2001	St Vincent and the Grenadines (REALM)	Mr Cenio Lewis	Senior High Commissioner	London
/07/2003	Turkmenistan	Mr Yazmurad N Seryaev	Ambassador	London
/01/2008	Honduras	Mr Ivan Romero-Martinez	Ambassador	London
/11/2009	Oman	Mr Abdul Aziz Al Hinai	Ambassador	London
/01/2010	Monaco	Mrs Evelyne Genta	Ambassador	London
/01/2011	St Christopher & Nevis (REALM)	Dr Kevin Isaac	High Commissioner	London
/08/2011	Papua New Guinea (REALM)	Ms Winnie Anna Kiap CBE	High Commissioner	London
/08/2012	Samoa (NR)	Fatumanava Dr Pa'olelei H Luteru	High Commissioner	Brussels
/09/2014	Eritrea	Mr Estifanos Habtemariam Ghebreyesus	Ambassador	London
/11/2014	Venezuela	Ms Rocio Maneiro	Ambassador	London
/01/2015	Nicaragua	Ms Guisell Morales-Echaverry	Ambassador	London
/01/2015	Djibouti (NR)	Mr Ayeid Mousseid Yahya	Ambassador	Paris
/06/2015	Yemen	Dr Yassin Saeed Noman Ahmed	Ambassador	London
/08/2015	Mauritius	Mr Girish Nunkoo	High Commissioner	London
/09/2015	Bahrain	Shaikh Fawaz Bin Mohamed Al Khalifa	Ambassador	London
/09/2015	Gabon	Mrs Aichatou Sanni Aoudou	Ambassador	London
/01/2016	Antigua and Barbuda (REALM)	Ms Karen-Mae Hill	High Commissioner	London
/01/2016	Fiji	Mr Jitoko Tikolevu	High Commissioner	London
/06/2016	Tanzania	Dr Asha-Rose Migiro	High Commissioner	London
/08/2016	Albania	Mr Qirjako Qirko	Ambassador	London
/09/2016	Portugal	Mr Manuel Lobo Antunes	Ambassador	London
/11/2016	Korea (DPR)	Mr Choe Il	Ambassador	London
/12/2016	Jamaica (REALM)	Mr Seth Ramocan	High Commissioner	London
02/2017	The Philippines	Mr Antonio Manuel Lagdameo	Ambassador	London
/02/2017	Kazakhstan	Mr Erlan Abilfayizuly Idrissov	Ambassador	London
/02/2017	Congo (Democratic Republic of)	Ms Marie Ndjeka Opombo	Ambassador	London
/03/2017	Thailand	Mr Pisanu Suvanajata	Ambassador	London
/04/2017	Paraguay	Mr Genaro Vicente Pappalardo Ayala	Ambassador	London
/08/2017	Luxembourg	Mr Jean Olinger	Ambassador	London
/08/2017	Lithuania	Mr Renatas Norkus	Ambassador	London
/08/2017	Uganda	Mr Julius Peter Moto	High Commissioner	London
/08/2017	Ireland	Mr Adrian O'Neill	Ambassador	London
/09/2017	Croatia	Mr Igor Pokaz	Ambassador	London
/09/2017	Denmark	Mr Lars Thuesen	Ambassador	London
/10/2017	Tunisia	Mr Nabil Ben Khedher	Ambassador	London
/11/2017	Lebanon	Mr Rami Mortada	Ambassador	London
/11/2017	The Bahamas (REALM)	Mr Ellison Edroy Greenslade	High Commissioner	London
/11/2017	Guinea	Mr Alexandre Cécé Loua	Ambassador	London
/01/2018	Italy	Mr Raffaele Trombetta	Ambassador	London
/02/2018	Niger (NR)	Mr Ado Elhadji Abou	Ambassador	Paris
/03/2018	South Africa	Ms Nomatemba Gugulethu Pudnixia Olivia Tambo	High Commissioner	London
/04/2018	Australia (REALM)	The Hon George Henry Brandis QC	High Commissioner	London
/05/2018	Tonga	The Hon Titilupe Fanetupouvava'u Tu'ivakanō	High Commissioner	London
/06/2018	Zimbabwe	Col Christian Katsande	Ambassador	London
/08/2018	Burkina Faso (NR)	Mrs Jacqueline Zaba Nikiema	Ambassador	Brussels
/08/2018	Austria	Dr Michael Zimmermann	Ambassador	London
/08/2018	Chile	Mr David Gallagher	Ambassador	London
/09/2018	North Macedonia	Mrs Aleksandra Miovska	Ambassador	London
/09/2018	San Marino (NR)	Ms Silvia Marchetti	Ambassador	San Marino
09/2018	Turkey	Mr Ümit Yalçin	Ambassador	London
/09/2018	Moldova	Mrs Angela Ponomariov	Ambassador	London
/10/2018	Peru	Mr Juan Carlos Gamarra Skeels	Ambassador	London
/10/2018	Cameroon	Mr Albert Njoteh Fotabong	High Commissioner	London
/10/2018	Tuvalu (REALM NR)	Mr Aunese Makoi Simati	High Commissioner	UAE

09/10/2018	Brazil	Mr Claudio Frederico de Matos Arruda	Ambassador	London
31/10/2018	Costa Rica	Mr Rafael Ortiz Fábrega	Ambassador	London
14/11/2018	Kenya	Mr Manoah Esipisu	High Commissioner	London
26/11/2018	Bangladesh	Ms Saida Muna Tasneem	High Commissioner	London
04/12/2018	Serbia	Mrs Aleksandra Joksimović	Ambassador	London
17/12/2018	Barbados	Mr Milton Inniss	High Commissioner	London
19/12/2018	Namibia	Ms Linda Scott	High Commissioner	London
29/12/2018	Botswana	Dr John Gosiamemang Ndebele Seakgosing	High Commissioner	London
04/01/2019	Norway	Mr Wegger Strømmen	Ambassador	London
06/02/2019	Liberia	Mrs Gurly T Gibson	Ambassador	London
18/02/2019	Laos	Mr Phongsavanh Sisoulath	Ambassador	London
07/05/2019	Grenada (REALM)	Ms Lakisha Grant	High Commissioner	London
17/05/2019	Bulgaria	Mr Marin Raykov	Ambassador	London
22/05/2019	Maldives	Dr Farahanaz Faizal	High Commissioner	London
14/06/2019	United Arab Emirates	Mr Mansoor Abulhoul	Ambassador	London
01/07/2019	Saudi Arabia	HRH Prince Khalid bin Bandar bin Sultan Al Saud	Ambassador	London
05/07/2019	Suriname (NR)	Mr Reggy Martiales Nelson	Ambassador	Paris
06/08/2019	Kyrgyzstan	Mr Edil Baisalov	Ambassador	London
01/09/2019	Cyprus	Mr Andreas S Kakouris	High Commissioner	London
03/09/2019	Bosnia and Herzegovina	Mr Vanja Filipović	Ambassador	London
03/09/2019	France	Mrs Catherine Colonna	Ambassador	London
15/10/2019	Sierra Leone	Dr Morie Komba Manyeh	High Commissioner	London
23/10/2019	Uzbekistan	Mr Said Rustamov	Ambassador	London
31/10/2019	Iraq	Mr Mohammed Jaafar M Bakr Haidar Al-Sadr	Ambassador	London
06/11/2019	Panama	Mrs Irma Natalia Royo Ruiz de Hagerman	Ambassador	London
22/11/2019	Russia	Mr Andrei Kelin	Ambassador	London
06/12/2019	Senegal	Mrs Fatimata Dia	Ambassador	London
10/12/2019	Zambia	Lt Gen Paul Mihova	High Commissioner	London
16/01/2020	Angola	General Geraldo Sachipengo Nunda	Ambassador	London
14/02/2020	Cuba	Mrs Bárbara Elena Montalvo Alvarez	Ambassador	London
20/02/2020	European Union	Mr João Vale de Almeida	Ambassador	London
02/03/2020	Sri Lanka	Ms Saroja Sirisena	High Commissioner	London
06/04/2020	Georgia	Ms Sophie Katsarava MBE	Ambassador	London
11/05/2020	Hungary	Dr Ferenc Kumin	Ambassador	London
18/05/2020	Belgium	Mr Bruno van der Pluijm	Ambassador	London
20/06/2020	Brunei	First Admiral (Rtd) Pengiran Dato Seri Pahlawan Norazmi bin Pengiran Haji Muhammad	High Commissioner	London
22/06/2020	India	Ms Gaitri Issar Kumar	High Commissioner	London
16/07/2020	Latvia	Mrs Ivita Burmistre	Ambassador	London
03/08/2020	New Zealand (REALM)	Mr Bede Corry	High Commissioner	London
14/08/2020	Cote d'Ivoire	Mrs Sarah Affoue Amani	Ambassador	London
21/08/2020	Belarus	Mr Maxim Yermalovich	Ambassador	London
24/08/2020	Netherlands	Mr Karel van Oosterom	Ambassador	London
31/08/2020	Argentina	Mr Javier Esteban Figueroa	Ambassador	London
02/09/2020	Singapore	Mr Lim Thuan Kuan	High Commissioner	London
02/09/2020	Ukraine	Mr Vadym Prystaiko	Ambassador	London
07/09/2020	Uruguay	Dr César Rodríguez-Zavalla	Ambassador	London
10/09/2020	Cambodia	Mr Pharidh Kan	Ambassador	London
14/09/2020	Mauritania	Mr Sidya Ould Elhadi	Ambassador	London
14/09/2020	Pakistan	Mr Moazzam Ahmad Khan	High Commissioner	London
15/09/2020	Ethiopia	Mr Teferi Melesse Desta	Ambassador	London
22/09/2020	Slovenia	Ms Simona Leskovar	Ambassador	London
05/10/2020	Greece	Mr Ioannis Raptakis	Ambassador	London
07/10/2020	Israel	Mrs Tzipora (Tzipi) Hotovely	Ambassador	London
22/10/2020	Holy See	Archbishop Claudio Gugerotti	Apostolic Nuncio	London
04/11/2020	Andorra (NR)	Mr Carles Jordana Madero	Ambassador	Andorra
16/11/2020	Iceland	Mr Sturla Sigurjónsson	Ambassador	London
02/12/2020	Haiti	Mr Euvrard Saint Amand	Ambassador	London
08/12/2020	El Salvador	Ms Vanessa Interiano Elfarnawany	Ambassador	London
08/12/2020	Indonesia	Mr Desra Percaya	Ambassador	London
06/01/2021	Slovakia	Mr Róbert Ondrejcsák	Ambassador	London
18/01/2021	Afghanistan	Dr Zalmai Rassoul	Ambassador	London
16/02/2021	Japan	Mr Hajime Hayashi	Ambassador	London

Date	Country	Name	Title	Location
/03/2021	Romania	Mrs Daniela-Laura Popescu	Ambassador	London
/03/2021	Dominican Republic	Mr Elnio Manuel Durán	Ambassador	London
/03/2021	South Sudan	Ms Agnes Oswaha	Ambassador	London
/04/2021	Mexico	Ms Josefa González-Blanco	Ambassador	London
/04/2021	Canada (REALM)	Mr Ralph Goodale	High Commissioner	London
/04/2021	Mozambique	Mrs Albertina MacDonald	High Commissioner	London
/05/2021	Nigeria	Mr Sarafa Tunji Isola	High Commissioner	London
/06/2021	Guatemala	Mr Jose Alberto Briz Gutierrez	Ambassador	London
/06/2021	Viet Nam	Mr Nguyen Hoang Long	Ambassador	London
/06/2021	China	Mr Zheng Zeguang	Ambassador	London
/06/2021	Ghana	Mr Papa Owusu-Ankomah	High Commissioner	London
/07/2021	Iran	Mr Mohsen Baharvand	Ambassador	London
/07/2021	Korea, Republic of	Mr Gunn Kim	Ambassador	London
/07/2021	Belize (REALM)	Mrs Therese Rath	High Commissioner	London
/08/2021	Switzerland	Mr Markus Leitner	Ambassador	London
/08/2021	Malaysia	Mr Zakri Jaafar	High Commissioner	London
/08/2021	Estonia	Mr Viljar Lubi	Ambassador	London
/08/2021	Azerbaijan	Mr Elin Emin oglu Suleymanov	Ambassador	London
/08/2021	Sweden	Mrs Mikaela Kumlin Granit	Ambassador	London
/09/2021	Spain	Mr José Pascual Marco Martínez	Ambassador	London
/09/2021	Armenia	Mr Varuzhan Nersesyan	Ambassador	London
/09/2021	Finland	Mr Jukka Siukosaari	Ambassador	London
/09/2021	Jordan	Mr Manar Dabbas	Ambassador	London
/10/2021	Burundi	Mrs Elisa Nkerabirori	Ambassador	London
/10/2021	Trinidad and Tobago	Mr Vishnu Dhanpaul	High Commissioner	London
/10/2021	Malawi	Dr Thomas Bisika	High Commissioner	London
/10/2021	Ecuador	Mr Sebastian Corral Bustamánte	Ambassador	London
/11/2021	Somalia	Mr Abdulkadir Ahmed Kheyr Abdi	Ambassador	London
/12/2021	Mongolia	Mr Enkhsukh Battumur	Ambassador	London
/12/2021	Egypt	Mr Sherif Kamel	Ambassador	London
/12/2021	Algeria	Mr Lounès Magramane	Ambassador	London
/01/2022	Kosovo	Mr Ilir Kapiti	Ambassador	London
/01/2022	Tajikistan	Mrs Rukhshona Emomali	Ambassador	London
/01/2022	Morocco	Mr Hakim Hajoui	Ambassador	London
/01/2022	Qatar	Mr Fahad bin Mohammed Abdullah Abdullah Al-Attiyah	Ambassador	London
/02/2022	Chad (NR)	Mr Kedella Younous Hamidi	Ambassador	Paris

HER HEADS OF MISSION

	Palestinian Mission	Mr Husam S Zomlot	Head of Mission	London

ARGES D'AFFAIRES & ACTING HIGH COMMISSIONERS

Date	Country	Name	Title	Location
/12/2014	Dominica	Ms Janet Charles	Acting High Commissioner	London
/12/2016	Cabo Verde (NR)	Mr Octávio Gomes	Chargé d'Affaires	Brussels
/08/2017	Libya	Mr Mohamed A E Elkoni	Chargé d'Affaires	London
/12/2018	Equatorial Guinea	Ms Maria Jesús Diallo Besari	Chargé d'Affaires	London
/06/2019	Mali (NR)	Mrs Coulibaly Sira Cisse	Chargé d'Affaires	Brussels
/07/2019	Madagascar	Mrs Anjaniaina Olivia Rakotonirina	Chargé d'Affaires	London
/08/2019	Togo	Mr Komlanvi Agbenozan Dedji	Chargé d'Affaires	London
/12/2019	Guyana	Ms Pegy McLennan	Acting High Commissioner	
/12/2020	Seychelles	Mr Terry Romain	Acting High Commissioner	London
/04/2021	Burma	Dr Chit Win	Chargé d'Affaires	London
/05/2021	Sudan	Mr Khalid Mohamed Ali Hassan	Chargé d'Affaires	London
/06/2021	The Gambia	Mr Alieu Njie	Acting High Commissioner	London
/06/2021	Poland	Ms Agnieszka Kowalska	Chargé d'Affaires	London
/07/2021	Montenegro	Mr Mladen Dragasevic	Chargé d'Affaires	London
/07/2021	Malta	Dr Daniel Attard	Acting High Commissioner	London
/08/2021	USA	Mr Philip Reeker	Chargé d'Affaires	London
/08/2021	Czech Republic	Mr Aleš Opatrný	Chargé d'Affaires	London
/09/2021	Lesotho	Ms Lineo Palime	Acting High Commissioner	London
/09/2021	Rwanda	Mr James Wizeye	Acting High Commissioner	London
/09/2021	St Lucia	Mrs Leonne Theodore-John	Acting High Commissioner	London
/10/2021	Bolivia	Mr. Juan Carlos Crespo Montalvo	Chargé d'Affaires	

21/10/2021	Nepal	Mrs Roshan Khanal	Chargé d'Affaires	London
12/11/2021	Eswatini	Ms Temnotfo L.C. Nkambule	Acting High Commissioner	London
17/12/2021	Germany	Mrs Julia Gross	Chargé d'Affaires	London
31/12/2021	Colombia	Mr. Pedro Isidro López-Pérez	Chargé d'Affaires	London
28/01/2022	Timor-Leste	Mr Crisógno Leandro de Araújo	Chargé d'Affaires	
VACANT	Benin	VACANT	-	-
VACANT	Central African Republic (CAR)	VACANT	-	-
VACANT	Congo (Republic of)	VACANT	-	-
VACANT	Guinea-Bissau	VACANT	-	-
VACANT	Kiribati	VACANT	-	-
VACANT	Nauru	VACANT	-	-
VACANT	São Tomé & Principe	VACANT	-	-
VACANT	Solomon Islands	VACANT	-	-
VACANT	Somalia	VACANT	-	-
VACANT	Syria	VACANT	-	-
VACANT	Vanuatu	VACANT	-	-

NATIONAL DAYS

Date		Country	Title
January	1	Cuba	Day of Liberations
	1	Haiti	National Day
	1	Sudan	Independence Day
	4	Burma (Myanmar)	Independence Day
	26	India	Republic Day
	26	Australia	Australia Day
	31	Nauru	Independence Day
February	4	Sri Lanka	Independence Day
	6	New Zealand	Waitangi Day
	7	Grenada	Independence Day
	11	Iran	Islamic Revolution Day
	15	Serbia	National Day
	16	Lithuania	Independence Day
	17	Kosovo	Independence Day
	18	The Gambia	Independence Day
	23	Brunei	National Day
	23	Guyana	Republic Day
	23	Japan	Emperor's Birthday
	24	Estonia	Independence Day
	25	Kuwait	National Day
	27	Dominican Republic	Independence Day
March	1	Bosnia & Herzegovina	Independence Day
	3	Bulgaria	National Day
	6	Ghana	Independence Day
	12	Mauritius	Republic Day
	15	Hungary	National Day
	17	Ireland	St Patrick's Day
	20	Tunisia	Independence Day
	21	Namibia	National Day
	23	Pakistan	National Day
	25	Greece	Independence Day
	26	Bangladesh	Independence Day
April	4	Senegal	National Day
	16	Denmark	Royal Birthday
	17	Syria	National Day
	18	Zimbabwe	National Day
	19	Swaziland	Royal Birthday
	19	Holy See	Inauguration Day
	26	Israel	National Day
	26	Tanzania	Union Day
	27	Netherlands	National Day
	27	Sierra Leone	National Day
	27	South Africa	Freedom Day
	27	Togo	National Day
	30	Netherlands	Official Birthday
May	3	Poland	National Day
	5	Netherlands	Liberation Day
	15	Paraguay	Independence Day
	17	Norway	Constitution Day
	20	Cameroon	National Day
	22	Yemen	National Day
	24	Eritrea	National Day

	25	Jordan	Independence Day
	25	Argentina	National Day
	26	Guyana	Independence Day
	26	Georgia	Independence Day
	28	Azerbaijan	National Day
	28	Ethiopia	National Day
	30	Croatia	National Day
June	1	Samoa	Independence Day
	2	Italy	National Day
	5	Denmark	Constitution Day
	6	Sweden	National Day
	10	Portugal	National Day
	12	Russia	National Day
	12	Philippines	National Day
	17	Iceland	National Day
	23	Luxembourg	National Day
	25	Mozambique	National Day
	25	Slovenia	National Day
	26	Madagascar	Independence Day
	27	Djibouti	National Day
	29	Seychelles	National Day
	30	Democratic Republic of Congo	National Day
July	1	Burundi	National Day
	1	Somalia	National Day
	1	CF	National Day
	1	Rwanda	National Day
	1	British Virgin Islands	Territory Day
	3	Belarus	National Day
	4	Tonga	National Day
	4	United States	Independence Day
	5	Algeria	National Day
	5	Cabo Verde	National Day
	5	Venezuela	Independence Day
	6	Malawi	National Day
	9	South Sudan	National Day
	10	Bahamas	National Day
	11	Mongolia	National Day
	12	São Tome & Principe	National Day
	12	Kiribati	Independence Day
	14	France	National Day
	15	Brunei	Royal Birthday
	17	Lesotho	Royal Birthday
	20	Colombia	Independence Day
	21	Belgium	National Day
	23	Egypt	National Day
	26	Maldives	National Day
	26	Liberia	Independence Day
	28	Peru	National Day
	30	Vanuatu	Independence Day
	30	Morocco	Date of Accession
August	1	Benin	National Day
	1	Switzerland	National Day
	2	North Macedonia	National Day
	6	Bolivia	Independence Day
	6	Jamaica	Independence Day
	7	Côte d'Ivoire	National Day
	9	Singapore	National Day

10	Ecuador	Independence Day
11	Chad	Independence Day
15	Republic of Congo	National Day
15	Liechtenstein	National Day
17	Gabon	National Day
17	Indonesia	National Day
19	Afghanistan	National Day
20	Hungary	National Day
24	Ukraine	Independence Day
25	Uruguay	Independence Day
27	Moldova	National Day
31	Trinidad & Tobago	Independence Day
31	Kyrgyzstan	Independence Day
31	Malaysia	National Day

September

1	Slovak Republic	Constitution Day
1	Uzbekistan	Independence Day
1	Libya	National Day
2	Vietnam	National Day
3	San Marino	National Day
6	Swaziland	National Day
7	Brazil	Independence Day
8	Andorra	National Day
8	North Macedonia	Independence Day
9	Democratic People's Republic of Korea	National Day
9	Tajikistan	Independence Day
15	Guatemala	Independence Day
15	Costa Rica	Independence Day
15	El Salvador	Independence Day
15	Honduras	Independence Day
15	Nicaragua	Independence Day
16	Mexico	Independence Day
16	Papua New Guinea	National Day
16	St Christopher & Nevis	National Heroes Day
18	Chile	National Day
19	St Christopher & Nevis	Independence Day
20	Nepal	National Day
21	Malta	National Day
21	Armenia	National Day
21	Belize	National Day
22	Mali	National Day
23	Saudi Arabia	National Day
24	Guinea-Bissau	National Day
30	Botswana	Botswana Day

October

1	Nigeria	National Day
1	China	National Day
1	Cyprus	Independence Day
1	Palau	Independence Day
2	Guinea	National Day
3	Germany	National Day
3	Korea	National Day
4	Lesotho	Independence Day
9	Uganda	Independence Day
10	Fiji	National Day
12	Spain	National Day
12	Equatorial Guinea	National Day
23	Hungary	National Day
24	Zambia	Independence Day

24	United Nations Day	
26	Austria	National Day
27	Saint Vincent & the Grenadines	Independence Day
27	Turkmenistan	Independence Day
28	Czech Republic	National Day
29	Turkey	National Day

November

1	Antigua & Barbuda	National Day
1		National Day
3	Panama	Independence Day
3	Commonwealth of Dominica	Independence Day
4	Tonga	Constitution Day
9	Cambodia	National Day
11	Angola	Independence Day
18	Latvia	National Day
18	Oman	National DAy
19	Monaco	National Day
22	Lebanon	National Day
25	Suriname	National Day
28	Mauritania	Independence Day
28	Albania	National Day
30	Barbados	National Day

December

1	Romania	National Day
1	Central Africa Republic	National Day
2	United Arab Emirates	National Day
2	Laos	National Day
5	Thailand	Royal Birthday
6	Finland	National Day
11	Burkina Faso	National Day
12	Kenya	Independence Day
12	Turkmenistan	Day of Turkmenistan Neutrality
16	Bahrain	National Day
16	Kazakhstan	Independence Day
18	Niger	National Day
18	Qatar	National Day

DIRECTORY OF
INTERNATIONAL ORGANISATIONS

International Organisations & their staff do not enjoy privileges & immunities under the Diplomatic Privileges Act 1964 but under separate legislation, to which reference is made in each entry in this Directory.

m   Married
*   Married but not accompanied by wife or husband

CAB INTERNATIONAL
(International Organisations Acts 1968 & 1981-S.I. 1982/1071)
Wallingford Oxon OX10 8DE
01491 832111
Fax 01491 833508
corporate@cabi.org
www.cabi.org

Dr Trevor Nicholls m *Chief Executive Officer*
Mr Robert Sloley m *Chief Finance Officer*
Ms Caroline McNamara m *Chief Commercial Officer*
Mr Neil MacIntosh m *Executive Director, Human Resources*
Dr Ulrich Kuhlmann m *Executive Director, Global Operations*
Dr Dennis Rangi m *Director General, Development*
Dr Andrew Robinson, m *Managing Director Publishing*
Dr Qiaoqiao Zhang m Memberships *Director*
Mr André Laperriere m *Executive Director, GODAN*

COMMONWEALTH FOUNDATION
(International Organisations Act, 1968-S.I. 1983/143)
East Wing Marlborough House Pall Mall SW1Y 5HY
020 7747 6579
FAX 020 7839 8157
www.commonwealthfoundation.com

Dr Anne Therese Gallagher **m** *Director-General*
Mr Shem Odhiambo Ochola **m** *Deputy Director-General*

COMMONWEALTH SECRETARIAT
(Commonwealth Secretariat Act, 1966)
Marlborough House Pall Mall SW1Y 5HX
020 7747 6500
FAX 020 7930 0827
www.thecommonwealth.org

HER EXCELLENCY BARONESS PATRICIA JANET SCOTLAND **m** *Commonwealth Secretary-General*
      Mr Richard Martin Mawhinney spouse
Mr Arjoon Suddhoo **m** *Deputy Secretary-General*
Mr Paulo Kautoke **m** *Senior Director (Trade, Oceans & Natural Resources)*
Professor Luis Franceschi *Senior Director (Governance & Peace)*
Dr Umakant Panwar **m** *Interim Director (Human Resources and Facilities Management)*
Mr Mark Albon **m** *Head (Countering Violent Extremism Unit)*
Mr Nick Hardman-Mountford **m** *Head (Oceans and Natural Resources)*
Ms Pamella McLaren **m** *Adviser & Head (Debt Management)*
Mrs Evelyn Pedersen **m** *Head (Strategy, Learning and Evaluation)*
Dr Brendan Vickers *Adviser & Head International Trade Policy*
Mr Abhik Sen **m** *Head (Policy & Research)*
Ms Carina Kabajunga *Head (Information and Communication Technology)*

Mr Unnikrishnan Nair m Head *(Climate Change)*
Mrs Opeyemi Abebe Adviser & Head *(Trade Competitiveness Section)*
Mr Kirk Haywood *Adviser & Head (Commonwealth Connectivity Agenda Section)*
Ms Chantal Sciberras *Adviser & Head (Europe)*
Ms Dinusha Panditaratne Adviser & Head *(Asia)*

COMMONWEALTH TELECOMMUNICATIONS ORGANISATION
(International Organisations Acts 1968 & 1981-S.I. 1983/144)
64-66 Glenthorne Road W6 OLR
Tel: 020 8600 3800
Fax: 020 8600 3819
www.cto.int
SG.Office@cto.int

Ms Bernadette Lewis *Secretary General*

THE EUROPEAN BANK FOR RECONSTRUCTION & DEVELOPMENT
(International Organisations Act, 1968-S.I. 1991/757)
1 Exchange Square EC2A 2JN
020 7338 6000
Fax 020 7338 6100
www.ebrd.com

Mrs Odile Renaud-Basso m *President*
Jürgen Rigterink 'm *1st Vice-President & Head of Client Services Group*
Soha El-Turky **m** *Chief Finance Officer*
Alain Pilloux **m** *Vice-President, Banking*
Annemarie Straathof **m** *Vice-President, Risk & Compliance Chief Risk Officer*
Mark Bowman **m** *Vice-President, Policy & Partnership*
Dina Matta **m** *Vice-President, Chief Transformation Officer*

EUROPEAN CENTRE FOR MEDIUM-RANGE WEATHER FORECASTS (ECMWF)
(International Organisations Act, 1968 & 1981-S.I. 1975/158)
Shinfield Park Reading Berkshire RG2 9AX
0118 949 9000
Fax 0118 986 9450
www.ecmwf.int

Dr Florence Rabier **m** *Director-General*
Dr Andrew Brown **m** *Director of Research Department & Deputy Director-General*
Dr Florian Pappenberger **m** *Director of Forecasts Department*
Mr Luiz de Castro Neves **m** *Director of Administration Department*
Dr Martin Palkovic **m** *Director of Computing Department*

EUROPEAN GNSS AGENCY
NATS Swanwick Centre
Sopwith Way
Swanwick
Hampshire
SO31 7AY
Tele: +44(0)2380401958
Email: jose.castellomoreno@gsa.europa.eu

Mr Jose Castello-Moreno **m** *GSMC Security Implementation Officer*

EUROPEAN INVESTMENT BANK
(European Communities Act, 1972-Protocol on the Privileges & Immunities of the European Communities, 1965)
125 Old Broad Street, London EC2N 1AR
0207 367 5950
Email: londonoffice@eib.org
Fax +352 4379 60118
www.eib.org

Mr Carsten Morgenstern m *Head of Office*
Mrs Luisa Morici m *Coordination Officer*

EUROPEAN MOLECULAR BIOLOGY LABORATORY (UK SITE)
EUROPEAN BIOINFORMATICS INSTITUTE (EMBL-EBI)
(International Organisations Act, 1968 & 1981-S.I. 1994-1890)
Wellcome Genome Campus Hinxton Cambridge CB10 1SD
01223 494444
Fax 01223 494468

Professor Edith Heard f *Director-General of EMBL (Non-Resident)*
Dr Ewan Birney m *Director of EMBL-EBI*
Dr Rolf Apweiler m *Director of EMBL-EBI*
Dr Rachel Curran f *Head of Administration & Operations EMBL-EBI*

EUROPEAN SPACE AGENCY
(International Organisations Act, 1968-S.I.1978/1105)
Fermi Avenue
Harwell Campus Didcot OX11 OFD
01235 4444 200
www.esa.int

Mrs Elodie VIAU * *Head of ECSAT & Director of Telecommunications and Integrated Applications*
Mr Nicholas John Appleyard m *Deputy Head of ECSAT & Head of Integrated Applications and Downstream Services Department*

HONG KONG ECONOMIC & TRADE OFFICE
(International Organisations Act, 1968-S.I.1997/1334)
18 Bedford Square
London WC1B 3JA
020 7499 9821
Fax 020 7323 2336
general@hketolondon.gov.hk
www.hketolondon.gov.hk

Mr Sun On Law **m** *Director-General*
Ms Noel Kai Yin Ng **m** *Deputy Director-General 1*
Miss Josephine Hiu Tung Tsang *Deputy Director-General 2*
Mr Jeff Yan Ho Fong **m** *Assistant Director-General*
Mr Siu Man Chun **m** *Marine Adviser*
Mr Gary Hung Fai Tang *Deputy Marine Adviser 1*
Mr Derek Wing Tak Mak **m** *Deputy Marine Adviser 2*
Ms Jessica Ting Kam **m** *Deputy Head Investment*
End

HONG KONG ECONOMIC & TRADE OFFICE
(International Organisations Act, 1968-S.I.1997/1334)
18 Bedford Square
London WC1B 3JA
020 7499 9821
Fax 020 7323 2336
general@hketolondon.gov.hk
www.hketolondon.gov.hk

Mr Sun On Law m *Director-General*
Miss Josephine Hiu Tung Tsang Deputy Director-General 2
Mr Jeff Yan Ho Fong m *Assistant Director-General*
Mr Siu Man Chung m *Marine Adviser*
Mr Gary Hung Fai Tang *Deputy Marine Adviser 1*
Mr Derek Wing Tak Mak m *Deputy Marine Adviser 2*
Ms Jessica Ting Kam m *Deputy Head Investment*

INTERNATIONAL BANK FOR RECONSTRUCTION & DEVELOPMENT
(see under WORLD BANK GROUP)

INTERNATIONAL COFFEE ORGANIZATION
(International Organisations Act, 1968-S.I. 1969/733)
222 Gray's Inn Road, 4th floor, London, WC1X 8HB
020 7612 0600
Fax: 020 7612 0630
info@ico.org
www.ico.org

MR JOSE SETTE m *Executive Director*
Mr Gerardo Patacconi *Head of Operations*
Ms Tomoko Hayashi *Head of Finance and Administration*

INTERNATIONAL DEVELOPMENT ASSOCIATION
(see under WORLD BANK GROUP)

INTERNATIONAL FINANCE CORPORATION
(Overseas Development & Co-operation Act 1980-S.I. 1955/1954 S.I. 1976/221)
020 7592 8400
www.ifc.org
Mr Ignacio De Calonje *Chief Investment Officer*

INTERNATIONAL GRAINS COUNCIL
(International Organisations Act, 1968 & 1981-S.I. 1968/1863)
1 Canada Square Canary Wharf E14 5AE
020 7513 1122
Fax 020 7513 0630
igc@igc.int
www.igc.int

MR ARNAUD PETIT m *Executive Director*
Mr D Cooper m *Senior Economist*
Mr N Kemp m *Senior Economist*
Mr A Karavaytsev m *Senior Economist*

Ms M Morath **m** *Economist*

INTERNATIONAL MARITIME ORGANIZATION
(International Organisations Act, 1968-S.I. 2002/1826)
4 Albert Embankment SE1 7SR
020 7735 7611
Fax 020 7587 3210
www.imo.org

Mr KI TACK LIM **m** *Secretary-General*
Mrs Jung-ae **DO**
Mr F J Kenney *Director, Legal Affairs & External Relations Division (L.E.D.)*
Mrs H Deggim *Director, Maritime Safety Division (M.S.D.)*
Mr H Yamada **m** *Director, Conference Division (C.D.)*
Mr A Dominguez Velasco *Director, Marine Environment Division (M.E.D.)*
Mr X Zhang **m** *Director, Technical Cooperation Division (T.C.D.)*
Mr V Job **m** *Acting Director, Administration Division (A.D.)*
Mr J Westwood-Booth **m** *Senior Deputy Director, Sub-Division for Marine Technology &*
Cargoes, M.S.D.
Mr J Matheickal **m** *Deputy Director, Department of Partnerships & Projects (D.P. & P.)*
Ms P Charlebois *Deputy Director, Subdivision for Implementation, M.E.D.*
Mrs D Lost-Sieminska **m** *Deputy Director/Head, Legal Affairs Office, L.E.D.*
Mr J A Van der Graaf **m** *Deputy Director, Subdivision for Operational Safety and Human Element, M.S.D.*
Mr T Huang **m** *Deputy Director, Subdivision for Protective Measures, M.S.D.*
Mr P Sophocleous *Chief, Central Support Services, A.D.*
Mr J Pace **m** *Chief, Subdivision for Programme Management and Coordination, T.C.D.*
Mrs A Prempeh **m** *Chief of Staff, Office of the Secretary-General, O.S.G.*

THE FOLLOWING MEMBERS OF THE INTERNATIONAL MARITIME ORGANIZATION HAVE DESIGNATED PRINCIPAL PERMANENT REPRESENTATIVES TO THE ORGANIZATION IN THE UNITED KINGDOM:-

Brazil
170 Upper Richmond Road
London SW15 2SH
020 8246 4493/82
Fax 020 8246 4495
fianRepresentation.IMO@mar.org.uk

Admiral Luiz Henrique Caroli **m** *Permanent Representative*
Commander Vagner Belarmino de Oliveira **m** *Assistant to the Alternate Permanent Representative*

France
6 Cromwell Place London
London SW7 2JN
020 7073 1393
Fax : 020 7073 1294

Mrs Genevieve Jean-Van Rossum **m** *Permanent Representative*
Mr Damien Chevallier **m** *Deputy Permanent Representative*
Mr Philippe Janvier **m** *Alternate Permanent Representative*

Republic of Liberia
3rd Floor, 107 Fenchurch Street
London EC3M 5JF
020 7702 1243

Fax 020 7702 2639
info@liberianpm.org.uk

Mr Moses Owen Browne m *Permanent Representative*

Russian Federation
37 Harrington Gardens
London SW7 4JU
020 7370 6768/64
Fax 020 7370 0225
imo@mintrans.ru

Mr Yury Melenas m *Permanent Representative*

Vanuatu
Unit 210 – 95 Wilton Road
London SW1V 1BZ
07554 380 005

Mr Laurent Alain Parente *Permanent Representative*

INTERNATIONAL MOBILE SATELLITE ORGANIZATION
(International Organisations Act, 1968 & 1981-S.I. 1999/1125)
4 Albert Embankment, London, SE1 7SR, United Kingdom
020 3970 1060
www.imso.org
info@imso.org

Captain MOIN UDDIN AHMED m *Director General*
        Dr (Mrs) Farzana Ahmed
Mr Halil Ibrahim Keskin m *Technical Officer*
Mr Pier Giovanni Taranti m *Technical Officer*
Mrs Nadia Temple m *Administration and Finance Officer*

INTERNATIONAL OIL POLLUTION COMPENSATION FUNDS
(International Organisations Acts, 1968 & 1981 - S.I. 1979/912 & S.I. 1996/1295)
4 Albert Embankment, London, SE1 7SR, United Kingdom
020 7592 7100
info@iopcfunds.org
www.iopcfunds.org

Mr Gaute Sivertsen m *Director*
Mr Ranjit S P Pillai m *Deputy Director/Head, Finance & Administration Department*
Mr Thomas Liebert m *Head, External Relations & Conference Department*
Ms Liliana Monsalve m *Head, Claims Department*
Mr Robert Owen m *Head, Information Technology Department*

INTERNATIONAL ORGANIZATION FOR MIGRATION
Mission in the United Kingdom of Great Britain & Northern Ireland
(International Organisations Act 1968 - S.I. 2008/3124)
10 Dean Farrar Street, London, SW1H 0DX, United Kingdom
020 7811 6000
iomuk@iom.int

"Vacant" *Chief of Mission*

INTERNATIONAL SUGAR ORGANIZATION
(International Organisations Act, 1968 & 1981-S.I. 1969/734)
1 Canada Square Canary Wharf Docklands E14 5AA
020 7513 1144
Fax: 020 7513 1146
finance-admin@isosugar.org

Mr José Orive m *Executive Director*
Mr James Lowe m *Head of Finance & Administration*
Mr Peter de Klerk m *Senior Economist*
Mr Pedro Arruda m *Senior Economist*

INTERNATIONAL TELECOMMUNICATIONS SATELLITE ORGANISATION (ITSO)
(International Organisations Act, 1968 & 1981-S.I. 1979/911)
ITSO - 3400 International Drive NW Washington DC 20008-3096 USA
(00)1 202 243 5096
itsomail@itso.int

Mr José Toscano *Director General & Chief Executive Officer*

INTERNATIONAL WHALING COMMISSION
(International Organisations Act, 1968-S.I. 1975/1210)
The Red House 135 Station Road Impington Cambridge CB24 9NP
01223 233971
www.iwc.int
secretariat@iwc.int

Dr Rebecca Lent * *Executive Secretary*

NORTH ATLANTIC SALMON CONSERVATION ORGANIZATION
(European Communities Act, 1972-S.1. 1985/1973)
11 Rutland Square Edinburgh EH1 2AS
0131 228 2551
hq@nasco.int
www.nasco.int

Dr Emma Hatfield *Secretary*

NORTH EAST ATLANTIC FISHERIES COMMISSION
(International Organisations Act, 1968-S.I. 1999/278)
Accurist House, 44 Baker Street, London, W1U 7AL
020 7631 0016
Fax 020 7149 9950
www.neafc.org
info@neafc.org

Dr Darius Campbell **m** *Secretary*

THE OSPAR COMMISSION
(International Organisations Act, 1968-S.I. 1979/914)

The Aspect
12 Finsbury Square, London EC2A 1AS
020 7430 5200
www.ospar.org
secretariat@ospar.org

MR DOMINIC PATTINSON m *Executive Secretary*
Dr Jo Foden m *Deputy Secretary*
Ms Lena Avellan *Deputy Secretary*
Mr Philip Stamp *Deputy Secretary*
Mrs Laura de la Torre Gutierrez m *Deputy Secretary*

OFFICE OF THE UNITED NATIONS HIGH COMMISSIONER FOR REFUGEES (UNHCR)
(International Organisations Act, 1968-S.I. 1974/1261)
Ground Floor, 10 Furnival Street, London EC4A 1AB
020 3761 9500
www.unhcr.org.uk
gbrlo@unhcr.org

Ms Rossella Pagliuchi-Lor m *Representative*
Mr Matthew Saltmarsh m *Senior External Relations Officer*
Mr Lawrence Bottinick m *Senior Legal Officer*

DIVISION OF EXTERNAL RELATIONS (DER)
020 3761 9500
Alison Tilbe m *Head of Unit (Goodwill Ambassador Programme)*
Michael Walton m *Chief of Section (Digital Engagement Section)*

PRIVATE SECTOR FUNDRAISING (PSFR)
020 3761 8094
Lydia Piddock m *PSFR Officer (EUR & ME)*
Hyeon Gyeong Cho m *Private Sector Partnerships Officer*

REGIONAL UNITED NATIONS INFORMATION CENTRE
(International Organisations Act, 1968-S.I. 1974/1261)
Office: Residence Palace Bloc C2. Rue de la Loi 155/1040 Brussels
0032 (0) 2 788 8484
Fax 0032 (0) 2 788 8485
Info@unric.org

Mrs Afsane Bassir-Pour m *Director*

UNITED NATIONS ENVIRONMENT PROGRAMME
WORLD CONSERVATION MONITORING CENTRE
(International Organisations Act, 1968 - S.I. 1974/1261)
219 Huntingdon Road Cambridge CB3 0DL
01223 277314
Fax 01223 277136
www.unep-wcmc.org

Mr Neville Ash m *Director*
     Ms Elaine Marshall
Mrs Cornelia Prestorius m *Deputy Director*

THE UNITED NATIONS WORLD FOOD PROGRAMME
(International Organisations Act, 1968 - S.I. 1974/1261)
10 Furnival Street, London, EC4A 1AB
020 3857 7414
http://www.wfp.org

Ms Elisabeth Faure m *Director*

WORLD BANK GROUP
6th floor, 1 Tudor Street, London, EC4Y 0AH
INTERNATIONAL DEVELOPMENT ASSOCIATION
INTERNATIONAL BANK FOR RECONSTRUCTION & DEVELOPMENT
(Overseas Development & Co-operation Act 1980-S.I. 1946/36 S.I. 1976/221)
(Overseas Development & Co-operation Act 1980-S.I. 1960/1383 S.I. 1976/221)
020 7592 8400
Fax: 020 7592 8420
www.worldbank.org

Mr Ian White *Special Representative to the UK and Ireland*

HONORARY CONSULS

*Alphabetical list of Honorary Consular representatives of Foreign States &
Commonwealth Countries not represented by a Diplomatic Mission in London.
The persons listed have certain Privileges & Immunities under the
Consular Relations Act 1968.*

BENIN

Vacant

BHUTAN
2 Windacres Warren Road Guildford GU1 2HG
01483 538 189
mrutland@aol.com

Mr Michael R. Rutland *Honorary Consul for Bhutan*

BURKINA FASO

Vacant *Honorary Consul for the Republic for Burkina Faso*

CABO VERDE (REPBULIC OF)
33 Buckthorne Road
London SE4 2DG
a.diasborges@googlemail.com

Ms Anne-Marie Dias Borges *Honorary Consul for Cabo Verde*

COMOROS (UNION OF)
11 Park Place St James's
London SW1A 1LP
07768 821 888
kchehabi@gmail.com

Mr Khaled Chehabi m *Honorary Consul for the Union of Comoros*

CONGO (REPUBLIC OF)
3rd Floor Holborn Gate (HRG) 26 Southampton Buildings WC2A 1PN
020 7922 0695
Fax 020 7401 2566/2545

Mr Louis Muzzu m *Honorary Consul for the Republic of Congo*

KIRIBATI
The Great House Llanddewi Rydderch Monmouthshire NP7 9UY
01873 840 375
mravellwalsh@btopenworld.com

Mr Michael Ravell Walsh **m** *Honorary Consul for the Republic of Kiribati*

NAURU
Romshed Courtyard Underriver Nr Sevenoaks Kent TN15 0SD
01732 746 061
nauru@weald.co.uk

Mr Martin W.L. Weston *Honorary Consul for the Republic of Nauru*

PALAU
Bankfoot Square Bankfoot Street Batley WF17 5LH
01924 470 786
Fax 01924 474 747
www.palauconsulate.org.uk

Mr Q Mohammed **m** *Honorary Consul for the Republic of Palau*

SAN MARINO
17 Saint Cross,
London EC1N 8UW
0203 4093096
Cons.londra@gov.

Mr Maurizio Bragagni *Honorary Consul for San Marino*

SAMOA
Church Cottage Pedlinge Nr Hythe Kent CT12 5JL
01303 260 541
Fax 01303 238 058

Mr Fereti Tuilagi *Honorary Consul for Samoa*

SAO TOME & PRINCIPE
11 Briary Court,
Turner Street,
London E16 1AN
Tel: 07977 260564
chris.buckwell@btopenworld.com

Mr Chris Buckwell *Honorary Consul for Sao Tome & Principe*

SURINAME
127 Pier House
31 Cheyne Walk
London SW3 5HN
020 3084 7143
07768 196 326
Fax: 020 7349 0663

Mr Amwedhkar Jethu *Honorary Consul for Suriname*

TUVALU
Tuvalu House

230 Worple Road
London SW20 8RH
020 8879 0985
07466987616
tuvaluconsulate@netscape.net

Sir Iftikhar Ayaz *Honorary Consul for Tuvalu*

VANUATU
2/F
25 Thurloe Street
London SW7 2LQ
07565 197 840
james.eharris@vanuatuconsulate.uk

Mr James Maxwell Harris *m* *Honorary Consul for the Republic of Vanuatu*

CAREER CONSULS-GENERAL & CONSULS

Alphabetical list of Career Consular representatives of Foreign States & Commonwealth Countries notified under the Vienna Convention on Consular Relations. The persons listed have certain Privileges or Immunities under the Consular Relations Act, 1968.

AUSTRALIA

Agent General for South Australia
Australia Centre Cnr Melbourne Place & the Strand WC2B 4LG
020 7520 9100

Mr John David Ridgway m *Agent General for South Australia*

Agent General for Queensland
Australia Centre Cnr Melbourne Place & the Strand WC2B 4LG
020 7836 1333 or 020 7420 8761

Mrs Linda Anne Apelt m *Agent General for Queensland*

Agent General for Victoria
Australia Centre Cnr Melbourne Place & the Strand WC2B 4LG
020 7836 2656

Mr Kenneth John Ryan m *Agent General for Victoria*

Agent General for Western Australia
Australia Centre Cnr Melbourne Place & the Strand WC2B 4LG
020 7240 2881

Commodore Michael Deeks m *Agent General for Western Australia*

CANADA

Agent General for the Province of Québec
Québec House 59 Pall Mall London SW1Y 5JH
020 7766 5900

Mr John Coleman m *Agent General for Québec*

REPRESENTATIVES OF BRITISH OVERSEAS TERRITORIES

This list is provided for information only. Some of the persons listed below may have an entitlement to certain Privileges & Immunities.

ANGUILLA

Government of Anguilla London Office
The West India Committee
Suite 53, 3 Whitehall Court, Whitehall, SW1A 2EL
020 7799 5441
blondelcluff@westindiacommittee.org

Mrs Blondel Cluff *UK Representative*

BERMUDA

Government of Bermuda London Office
6 Arlington Street London SW1A 1RE
020 7518 9900
Fax: 020 7518 9901
www.gov.bm
kdurrant@gov.bm

Ms Kimberley Durrant *UK Representative*

BRITISH VIRGIN ISLANDS

Government of the British Virgin Islands London Office
BVI House 15 Upper Grosvenor Street W1K 7PJ
020 7355 9570
Fax 020 7355 9575
TBradshaw@bvi.org.uk
www.bvi.gov.vg

Ms Tracy Bradshaw Acting Director UK/EU Representative

CAYMAN ISLANDS

Cayman Islands Government Office in the United Kingdom
34 Dover Street W1S 4NG
020 7491 7772
Fax 020 7491 7944
tasha.ebanks-garcia@gov.ky
www.gov.ky

Dr Tasha Ebanks Garcia **m** *UK Representative*
Mr Charles G Parchment **m** *Deputy UK Representative*

FALKLAND ISLANDS

Falkland Islands Government Office
Falkland House 14 Broadway SW1H 0BH
020 7222 2542
Fax 020 7222 2375
representative@falklands.gov.fk

www.falklands.gov.fk

Mr Richard Hyslop **m** *UK Representative*

GIBRALTAR

Government of Gibraltar
150 Strand London WC2R 1JA
020 7836 0777
Fax 020 7240 6612
Info.london@gibraltar.gov.gi
www.gibraltar.gov.gi

Mr Dominique Searle MBE **m** *UK Representative*

MONTSERRAT

Government of Montserrat
52 Grosvenor Gardens
London
SW1W 0AU
020 7824 5125
j.panton@montserrat-gov.org

Mrs Janice Panton MBE **m** *UK Representative*

ST HELENA

Government of St Helena
Alliance House 12 Caxton Street SW1H 0QS
020 7031 0314
Fax 020 7031 0315
shgukrep@sthelenagov.com

Mrs Kedell Worboys MBE **m** *UK Representative*

TRISTAN da CUNHA

Government of Tristan da Cunha
29 Hulse Road
SALISBURY
SP1 3LU
ukrep@tdc.uk.com
ukadviser@tdc.uk.com

Mr Chris Carnegy *UK Representative*
Mr Jim Kerr *UK Adviser*

TURKS & CAICOS ISLANDS

Turks and Caicos Islands UK Representative
25 North Row
London
W1K 6DJ

Tel: +44(0)20 3691 6997
t.knight@tcilondon.org.uk

Ms Tracy Knight *UK Representative*

OTHER REPRESENTATIVE
OFFICES & ORGANISATIONS
IN THE UNITED KINGDOM

*This list is provided for information only. Some of the persons listed may
have certain privileges & immunities.*

THE LEAGUE OF ARAB STATES
106 Gloucester Place London W1U 6HU
Tel: 020 7317 0393
Fax: 020 7486 7586
press@arableague.org.uk

Mr Ibrahim Fouad Mohielden *Head of Mission*
Mr Sohail Elhouni *1st Secretary*
Mr Saleh Almari *Attaché*

INDEPENDENT INTERNATIONAL COMMISSION ON DECOMMISSIONING
I.I.C.D Block 1 Knockview Building Stormont Estate Belfast BT4 3SL
028 904 88600
Fax 028 904 88601

General John de Chastelain * *Chairman*
Mr Andrew D Sens * *Commissioner*
Brigadier-General Tauno Nieminen * *Commissioner*
Mr Aaro Suonio m *Chef de Cabinet*
Ms Ricki Schoen * *Office Manager*
Mrs Taina Suonio m *Administrative Assistant*

PALESTINIAN MISSION TO THE UNITED KINGDOM
5 Galena Road Hammersmith W6 0LT
020 8563 0008
Fax 020 8563 0058
www.palestinianmissionuk.com
info@palestinianmissionuk.com
info@palgd.org.uk

Dr Husam Zomlot m *Head of Mission*
      Mrs Suzan Zomlot
Miss Meisoon El-Shorafa *Political Affairs Counsellor*
Mrs Rana Abu Ayyash m *Consular Department*
